AMERICAN RED CROSS

LIFE SAVING
AND WATER SAFETY

Prepared by the American National Red Cross

WITH 142 ILLUSTRATIONS
UNDERWATER PICTURES MADE AT SILVER SPRINGS,
FLORIDA

24th PRINTING
November, 1968

DOUBLEDAY & COMPANY, INC.

GARDEN CITY, NEW YORK

THE MISSION OF THE RED CROSS

The American Red Cross is the instrument chosen by the Congress to help carry out the obligations assumed by the United States under certain international treaties known as the Geneva or Red Cross Conventions. Specifically, its Congressional charter imposes on the American Red Cross the duties to act as the medium of voluntary relief and communication between the American people and their armed forces, and to carry on a system of national and international relief to prevent and mitigate suffering caused by disasters.

All the activities of the American Red Cross and its chapters support these duties.

Nationally and locally the American Red Cross is governed by volunteers, most of its duties are performed by volunteers and it is financed by voluntary contributions.

The Lifesaving and Water Safety programs of the American National Red Cross, for which this book is a teaching text, stem from the Congressional charter provision that the organization shall devise and carry on measures for relieving and preventing suffering.

PREFACE

Safety in, on, and about the water depends upon a number of things. It begins, of course, with the ability to swim well enough to care for one's self under ordinary conditions. It does not, however, end there. Real water safety is also based upon such things as the ability to recognize and avoid hazardous water conditions and practices. Ability to use self-rescue skills to get out of dangerous situations is also a factor. Finally, skill in rescuing or assisting persons in danger of drowning is a means of preserving one's own life as well as saving that of someone else. The three major causes of drowning are, and always have been, failure to recognize hazardous conditions or practices, inability to get out of dangerous situations, and lack of knowledge of safe ways in which to aid or rescue drowning persons.

When Commodore Wilbert Longfellow, the great pioneer in water safety in the United States, started the Life Saving Service of the American Red Cross in 1914 the country was confronted by a tragic situation. People everywhere were flocking to the water in constantly increasing numbers, seeking recreation and enjoyment through bathing and water sports of various kinds. Their skill, however, fell far short of equaling their enthusiasm. As a result some 10,000 persons each year were losing their lives by drowning. This was due primarily to the fact that there were far too few supervised bathing places, too little opportunity to be taught how to swim skillfully for all who wished to learn, and practically no opportunity, except for lifeguards, to learn how to make a rescue or to resuscitate the apparently drowned. The literature on swimming and water sports was likewise scanty and far from adequate.

During the first 20 years of its existence the Life Saving Service of the Red Cross made a very important contribution to water safety in America, as it has ever since that time. During most of the early years its work and activity were supported by a unique little booklet named *Life Saving Methods,* which became known far and wide as "the lifesaver's bible." A surprising amount of useful information was contained in this little volume. The fact remains, however, that most of its content was devoted to exact descriptions of the rescue skills and the Schafer method of resuscitation, of which the Red Cross lifesaving tests were then composed.

As the work of the Life Saving Service grew in its first two decades, so did its experience and knowledge. Whereas at first Commodore Longfellow had concentrated wisely on the organization and training of volunteer lifesaving corps to supervise otherwise unguarded bathing places, it soon became evident that it was not the final answer to the problem. Soon, therefore, a subtle change in method became evident, which can best be summed up in the slogan coined by the Commodore: "Everyone a swimmer; every swimmer a lifesaver." This was recognition of the fact that the best kind of lifesaving lay in being able to take care of one's self in the water. It also recognized that the next-best way to cope with the drowning accident situation was to saturate the bathing scene with persons trained in lifesaving. Thus, whenever a drowning accident occurred, someone who knew what to do would be likely to be at the scene. Meanwhile, the store of knowledge and information grew as thousands of volunteer instructors and the small corps of experts on the national staff discovered or evolved new or better methods of preventing drowning accidents and saving lives. The little booklet *Life Saving Methods,* however inadequate, nevertheless still served as the basic text for the Service.

By 1933 it had become evident that a new and much more complete textbook was needed, into which could be gathered all of the water safety knowledge that the Service had accumulated. Finally in 1937 the first edition of this textbook was published.

Life Saving and Water Safety was planned and written as a resource to which anyone interested in water safety can refer, and from which a great deal of useful information can be gained. At the same time it is designed to be the textbook upon which Red Cross lifesaving training courses are based, to be used by both instructor and pupil as an authoritative source of knowledge and information.

In 1965 the annual drowning loss had decreased about one third to a figure of approximately 6,700. This figure, although still far too great, was remarkable because it has been achieved despite the fact that for every person engaging in water sports in 1914 there were a hundred or more in, on and about the water 50 years later. It is even more remarkable in that it pertains to almost the only major category of accidental deaths that has not actually increased in number of victims. Safer bathing places, more adequate supervision, and more opportunity to learn how to swim have contributed much to reduce the loss of life by drowning. So, too, have the efforts of a number of organizations acting either independently or in cooperation with the Red Cross. The knowledge and skill gained by many hundreds of thousands of persons through Red Cross water safety training, however, have played a very important part in making water sports less hazardous than they formerly were. Through the knowledge contained in this book and the efforts of thousands of volunteer instructors who use it as a teaching text, it is hoped that loss of life by drowning may continue its downward trend until drowning accidents become so rare as to cause wonder when they occur.

ACKNOWLEDGMENTS

This textbook has been written for the American Red Cross by Carroll L. Bryant who was for 27 years a member of the national staff of the Safety Services. For 7 years he served as national director of the Water Safety Service. Mr. Bryant is well qualified to write on the subject of Life Saving and Water Safety because of his training and experience in physical education, recreation and athletics. He is a widely recognized authority in the field of aquatics.

The Red Cross is grateful to the many volunteer water safety instructors and to the small group of devoted staff members and chapter directors who, through the years, have contributed so much to the fund of knowledge that is reflected in this book.

CONTENTS

AMERICAN RED CROSS
LIFE SAVING AND WATER
SAFETY

CHAPTER I

PERSONAL SAFETY IN SWIMMING

Man did not and does not naturally belong in the water. He lives, walks, eats and sleeps on land. His whole physical make-up, posture, body-temperature, breathing apparatus, shape and arrangement of arms and legs, specific gravity, functions, everything, has been developed and is arranged for terrestrial living. There is literally nothing to indicate that there is anything natural about his aquatic activities, yet an unbounded curiosity, a dominant will and a marvelously adaptable brain and physical structure have not only urged him into the water but have prompted him to develop a form of locomotion suited to his needs in the new element. He has found comfort, relaxation and enjoyment in the experience but at the same time experience has taught him that in the water there are definite limits beyond which he cannot safely go and that there is a certain amount of knowledge of water conditions which he must acquire.

Everyone knows certain basic facts about the water and about bathing. Water can suffocate (drown) a person if it closes over the mouth and nostrils for a more or less indefinite period of time; a few seconds in some cases, minutes in others. Like-

1

wise, it is well known that the length of time that a person can stay in the water without succumbing to exhaustion and exposure also has limits, depending upon the temperature of the water and the endurance of the individual. Some persons cannot stand more than a few minutes of immersion while others may stay in for several hours without ill-effect. It is common knowledge that to move about and to keep from drowning in deep water, one has to **learn** how to swim. No one, as far as the records show, ever walked directly into the water and swam away without previous knowledge of or practice in some form of swimming stroke. While it is quite true that any number of persons who could not swim have fallen or been pitched into deep water and yet were able by strenuous effort to keep their heads above water and in some cases actually made a little progress, the fact remains that they have not been at ease nor could they continue their efforts for very long.

These facts are fundamental and well known and need only to be repeated to children as they come to the age of understanding to insure a certain amount of water safety to the race. But this is not enough. The record down through the ages of the millions who have drowned, despite this basic knowledge, bears witness to the fact that there are other factors in aquatic experience that have to be considered. Although much has been accomplished in safeguarding the lives of those who bathe and a system of rescue has been worked out to aid those who get into difficulty, it is a fact that real safety in the water is largely a personal matter; that is, every person from the time he first enters the water until his taste for bathing ceases, should steadily acquire the knowledge and the skill which will enable him to take care of himself under all except the most unusual conditions.

So, it is to the sometimes well-known but too often unknown knowledge of water conditions and the skill employed in meeting emergencies, that this first part of the text is devoted. Every person who seeks recreation in the water needs to know certain things about being safe in the water from the time he takes his first plunge. As his aquatic skill increases, so should he parallel his development as a swimmer with certain definite safety skills which are wholly personal in nature; skills which will enable him to meet emergencies whether he ever has to face them or not.

The knowledge necessary for safety in bathing consists largely in knowing when, where, and how much to bathe. Skill for safety is made up of abilities to meet commonly hazardous conditions which beset the bather from time to time. This is the sum and substance of personal safety in the water.

When to Bathe.—There is very little question concerning the time of year in which to go bathing. In all-year pools and in southern latitudes where water temperatures are uniformly equable or vary only a few degrees at any time, a person bathes when he desires and wherever suitable water is available. Over a good part of the country, however, out-of-door bathing is limited to the summer months. In the middle latitudes, the season may be from May to October, while in the more northerly sections it is generally limited to July and August, although it is noted that, with favorable weather conditions thousands of bathers are beginning the season much earlier and continuing it much later than in former years. It is interesting to note the narrow temperature limits within which most persons find it comfortable to bathe. When the water ranges from seventy to seventy-eight degrees it is, apparently, most inviting to bathers. Many people will swim, of course, in water of higher temperature but often find it enervating. Only a comparatively small number of people, however, care to bathe when the temperature of the water falls below seventy degrees and these, as a rule, are hardy souls who have accustomed themselves to bathing in cold water. When the temperature of the water is somewhere in the sixties, there is great exhilaration in a plunge, but the output of energy to counter loss of body heat may bring about a state of exhaustion very rapidly.

A good part of the early season drowning loss is due directly to low temperature of the water and lack of good physical condition. Whenever there is a period of exceptionally warm weather in late spring or early in the summer there are always some (generally small boys) who decide that they would like to go swimming. The water is cold. They are naturally out of condition for swimming because of inactivity in the sport throughout the winter. Stimulated by the contact of cold water on the skin, they swim with more than the usual amount of vigor and govern the extent of the swim by what they could do when the season closed the previous year. The onset of fatigue may then be very rapid and if the person has, unwisely, swum away from shore and into deep water, his life will be imperiled.

The time of day when one should bathe is not particularly important when the bathing is done in enclosed, heated and well-lighted pools with one exception. The general rule for safety in the water which is that it is unwise to swim immediately after a meal applies in any case. Likewise, the fixed principle that one should not bathe alone also holds. Out-of-doors, the best swimming hours and the safest are the last two hours of the morning and like hours in the afternoon, although there is no grave danger to life or health involved in bathing in the early morning hours or at sunset and during twilight. On very hot days when the sunlight is very strong, bathing should be foregone during the middle of the day. Not that the water is bad for one at that time, but because exposure of the uncovered head to the direct rays of the sun and the glare of light upon the water may induce headache if nothing worse. Bathing at night is a thrilling experience and no one who has ever enjoyed a cooling dip just before retiring on a still, hot night can easily forget its pleasant qualities. When one swims well, knows thoroughly the place where he bathes, stays very close to shallow water and is accompanied by other swimmers, there is no real danger in a "star-light dip." If there is any risk involved it lies in striking obstructions, stepping off into holes or swimming too far off-shore.

The Morning Dip.—The "morning dip" is a subject about which a considerable amount of both sense and nonsense has been voiced. The "morning dip" is nothing more than a quick plunge taken immediately upon arising. Here again can be found real pleasure and exhilaration if the individual can stand the shock of cool air and cool water and reacts well to the experience. Some persons are rugged enough physically to enjoy a morning dip and benefit by it without any special preparation. Others can accustom themselves to it gradually by warming up easily before entering the water and by beginning with only the briefest periods of immersion. However, there are many to whom the quick transition from a warm bed to the chill morning air and the water is not only downright distasteful but quite lacking in benefit if not actually injurious to health. The harsh practice in some organized summer camps for children, of requiring every camper to take a "morning dip," which fortunately is rapidly dying out, was an example of an abuse in bathing which benefited the few and punished the majority. Briefly, it may be said that the "morning dip" should be made a matter of choice. If a person enjoys the experience, bears the shock easily and reacts well after the plunge, it is beneficial to him. If another person does not enjoy it but is organically sound and can stand the shock and reacts well even if belatedly, he can, if he wishes to, persist in the practice of taking "morning dips" and eventually derive benefit from it. All others should forego "morning dips" and do their bathing at times during the day when conditions are more to their liking.

Swimming after Eating.—Something must be said about a general rule for safety which has become almost axiomatic in this country and yet about which some confusion of thought exists. Briefly, it has been stated that a person should wait for an hour or an hour and a half after eating a meal before entering the water. Somewhat vaguely it is understood that the process of digestion and vigorous exercise do not go together and that a person may suffer a stomach cramp and drown as a result of going into the water too soon after eating. Not one iota of scientific evidence has ever been educed to prove that this is so, but unfortunate experience in thousands of cases clearly indicates that the rule is not without reason. No one knows exactly what happens in cases of stomach cramp and plenty of doubt still exists concerning its causes. However, this question is not nearly so important in relation to eating and swimming as another for which plenty of evidence exists.

Any physician, physical director, games instructor or coach would discourage anyone from indulging in golf, a strenuous tennis or squash match, a football, baseball or basketball game or any equally vigorous sport, immediately following the consumption of a hearty meal. There have been too many cases of nausea, indigestion and heart attacks noted in this connection. The same rule has not always been applied to swimming in the belief that it is a gentle exercise. Nothing could be further from the actual truth. Swimming is a vigorous exercise for more than ninety per cent of those who indulge in it. The novice, and he is predominant, works hard at his swimming in an effort to stay on the surface and make some progress. It is really only the experienced bather who knows how to stay afloat with very little effort.

It has been stated far too loosely that a person should "wait until his meal is **digested** before entering the water." This is not scientifically true. The time necessary for complete digestion is usually so long that there would be literally no time for swimming except for a few minutes immediately preceding the next meal. A better statement of fact would be "wait until the initial processes of digestion are well under way before entering the water" which would be well within the hour or hour and a half period usually prescribed.

A hearty meal fills the stomach with semi-solid material; not only fills it but causes it to distend beyond its normal dimensions when at rest. The process of distention causes the stomach to occupy more than its usual space in the abdomen and results in pressure upon the other organs, a condition to which adjustment is made normally without ill-effect. Everyone has experienced many times the feeling of drowsiness which develops after a substantial meal but many do not realize that this is nature's way of assuring a period of quiescence during which the process of liquefying the stomach content and preparing it for passage into the small intestine is the major activity of the body. While food remains in a semi-solid state and while the formation of gas may be contributing to the distention of the stomach, the pressure is more or less constant and violent exertion at such a time could, for example, cause the heart to labor unduly, frequently bringing about acute distress. Vigorous exercise may also arrest the process of digestion and greatly prolong the period in which the stomach remains distended. However, when the stomach content has been liquefied to a certain extent and any gas which may have been formed has been eliminated, the stomach returns to a somewhat normal state and the pressure is relieved. Then and then only is it really safe to enter the water to swim.

Although no definite proof can be elicited for the statement, it is reasonable to suspect that many of the drownings attributed to stomach cramp have actually been cases of heart-failure due to the combination of overexertion, and distress caused by abdominal distention.

Where to Bathe.—Literally thousands of safe bathing places are now available for use in this country. Tanks of both the indoor and out-of-door variety have been built by the hundreds during the past few years and there are uncounted thousands of bathing beaches along the shores of our many streams, rivers, ponds, lakes and seas.

Common sense should guide the bather in the selection of the place and the conditions under which he should enter the water. It should tell him that he is safest when under the observation of a life guard, teacher or a companion who is a swimmer, and in bathing areas where conditions of water, depths and bottom are known to be suitable for bathing. The non-swimmer should know that his activities are restricted to shallow water areas and that he should not bathe where there is a possibility of getting into deep water. He should resist at all times the temptation to venture beyond his depth with artificial support, that is, on planks, water wings, inner tubes or on the shoulders of a well-meaning but foolish swimming companion. If the unexpected happens and he loses that support, he has not the ability to regain the shore.

The novice, also, must confine his activities to areas in which he may quickly and easily reach safety if anything goes wrong. He should not overestimate his ability, or try something he is not sure he is capable of doing. The good swimmer, depending upon the state of advancement of his skill, may venture much more boldly than the novice but he, too, must govern his activity by the exercise of good judgment and knowledge of the possibility of accident circumstance which he cannot foresee. Also, he must remember that he is an ever present example to the non-swimmer and novice alike who seek to imitate his skill.

How Much to Bathe.—It is difficult to set arbitrary limits upon the length of time one should remain in the water. The usual controlled bathing period is generally set at one-half hour but even this is frequently shortened if conditions warrant. It would be unwise, however, to say that this should apply to all bathers since it is well known that there are many persons who can stand immersion for much longer periods. Furthermore, weather and water conditions may not only permit but actually invite a person to spend much more time in the water than is generally considered to be safe. The length of time a person may stay in the water without ill-effect is governed by the sense of physical comfort. Usually, when a person becomes chilled, enervated or tired he begins to feel uncomfortable and gets out of the water of his own volition. A survey of any bathing beach or pool will always show more persons out of the water than in it, indicating that people regulate of their own accord the amount of time they actually spend in the water. Only the relatively few, especially children, allow their sense of enjoyment to outweigh a growing feeling of discomfort, and prolong their periods of immersion unduly. If they are under control as, for example, at an organized summer camp, there is plenty of evidence actually visible to the supervisor to indicate that they have had enough. Uncontrollable shivering, a bluish tinge to the lips, a drawn or pinched face, cold and clammy skin, all tell the one in control that it is time for the person "to come out." These warning signs are easily recognizable, too, to the individual himself and should be heeded.

Physical Adjustment to Water.—Water of low temperature has different effects upon different persons. To the average individual in good health, the effect of entering it is one of only momentary maladjustment and temporary discomfort. To some

Fig. 1. Gradual immersion to adjust body to the water.

people, however, notably those who are of nervous temperament, those who have a tendency to anemia and those who are most commonly described as of "delicate" health, the shock of a plunge into cold water is not easily borne. Under such conditions breathing is inhibited even to the point, in some cases, where it may be stopped and the person may be quite unable to regain that function normally. Numbness may affect the arms and legs to such an extent that they may be temporarily paralyzed. A few, even though they are apparently organically sound, may be brought to a state of complete collapse from the effects of such an experience. Such persons should not swim when the temperature of the water is low, since by so doing they only invite trouble. In water of reasonable temperature (76–78°), however, there is little danger in bathing even for the delicate, if they will follow the practice of gradually immersing the body; walking in to mid-thigh depth, bending and dashing a little water in the face; rubbing water on the arms, in the arm-pits, on the back of the neck and on the chest; moving out to waist-depth and repeating the performance and only after some minutes getting wet all over.

Bathing periods should be limited to short dips until some resistance to cold is developed. Under certain sub-normal phys-ical conditions any bather, no matter how robust, may be af-fected by sudden immersion in much the same way. The same reactions may be brought about by entering the water when chilled, extremely tired or overheated. To avoid this difficulty, the swimmer should, in the first case, warm up by exercising for a few minutes or by rubbing with a coarse towel before he takes the plunge. When tired, rest is essential prior to entering the water and when overheated time should be allowed in which to cool down and relax.

Panic.—Panic, that sudden unreasoning and overwhelm-ing fear which attacks people in the face of real or fancied dan-ger, is a contributory cause to practically all water accidents. In swimming, it is, of course, motivated by the thought of drowning and attacks most commonly the non-swimmer and the novice, though the skilled swimmer is by no means im-mune. The tendency to panic should be resisted steadfastly by all bathers, who should remember that it cannot do any good but, rather, increases the hazard. The non-swimmer who loses his footing in shallow water, should concern himself wholly with regaining his feet, getting his head above water and mov-ing out of the situation until he has a chance to recover his breath and his wits. The novice and the swimmer in seeming peril must determine whether the danger is real or fancied, and if genuine, employ all their ability and intelligence to extricating themselves. For example, one of the commonest causes of panic among unskilled swimmers is induced by the motion of the waves. Even a skilled swimmer whose swimming ability has been developed in the quiet waters of a tank, may become panicky in open water when he observes as he swims toward shore that the waves are apparently running against him. This condition frequently occurs when the wind is offshore. Alarmed by the illusion that he is being carried away from shore he becomes terror stricken and either struggles until he is exhausted or becomes paralyzed by fear. A little reflection would cause him to remember that wave motion travels but the water does not and if he needs proof he has but to fix his gaze upon some stationary object to convince himself that he is making progress as he swims.

Exhaustion.—Another common contributory cause to water accidents is exhaustion. It is simply, loss of energy and resultant inability to make the necessary movements to keep afloat and make progress. This condition may be brought about by entering the water when overtired from some physical activity indulged in prior to the swim, overexertion in swimming or reaction to cold water. In the first case, a period of rest and recovery before entering the water is the normal requirement to insure reasonable safety. In the second case the swimmer, provided he is healthy and organically sound, can and will exert himself to the utmost; but either he should know when to rest or he should so direct his course that he may reach the shore before his energies are entirely dissipated. A buoyant person with good floating ability may rest by turning on the back and floating relaxed and motionless but even though the effort may in this way be prolonged it must be remembered that the lower temperature of the water is sapping the energy of the swimmer, making complete recovery in such intervals virtually impossible. This should quite discourage the practice of swimming long distances offshore, even by skilled swimmers, unless they are accompanied by boat. The practice of swimming long distances even in pairs would be discontinued by good swimmers if they would remember that if one reaches a point of exhaustion, the partner may be in a like condition and quite unable to give assistance or effect a rescue.

Water of low temperature, despite the fact that the swimmer may have adjusted himself physically to it, demands great expenditure of energy to resist the cold. Those who have experienced the leaden drag of arms, and the inability to relax cold and deadened muscles, do not have to be told that swimming in cold water should be confined to brief plunges or dips close to shore.

Progressive Development of Swimming Skill as a Factor in Water Safety.—The will to achieve swimming feats of endurance, speed and skill seems always to outstrip the development of ability to perform, except among those who are by nature habitually cautious. The offshore float, the other side of the pool, stream or small lake seem to offer a constant challenge to the bather and prompts him to attempt the crossing before he is prepared for it. Likewise, there is the challenge ever present in the activities of the swimmer more skilled than one's self. The good swimmer's skill on the diving board and apparent indifference to water conditions often causes the less skilled to attempt to emulate his activities, frequently with disastrous result. This tendency to venture foolishly must be resisted to prevent accident. At the same time, the challenge should stimulate the bather to learn progressively the skills which will enable him to meet it.

The non-swimmer should seek to learn such crude beginning swimmer movements as will enable him to stay afloat and navigate to a limited extent. The beginner should studiously apply himself to acquiring and practicing a standard swimming stroke or two which will permit him to step along to the novice class. The novice will seek the perfection of his limited equipment of strokes to develop ease in swimming and some endurance in order that he may one day style himself a swimmer. When one reaches the swimmer stage there is apparently no limit to the aquatic activities to which he can apply himself. Strokes to meet every bathing need, stunt swimming skills, dives and fancy dives; there is enough to keep one occupied for many years striving to reach that enviable state that so few attain, the position of an all-round swimmer. No one needs to remain for very long a standing bather, a beginner or a novice, when modern teaching methods and practice can be combined so readily as to enable a person to make steady progress in swimming and diving. (The stage of advancement from intermediate swimmer to swimmer will be slower.) As the individual makes progress, the challenges previously mentioned can be met and passed successively and safely. The skilled swimmer is less prone to accident than any other frequenter of the water. He is, as a rule, more keenly aware of what causes water accidents, has a more accurate knowledge of his capabilities and limitations and is less foolhardy than any other classification of bather. Physical limitations will always restrict the development of swimming skill for many bathers, yet every step taken in progressive learning and every handicap overcome will put the bather that much nearer the final goal and will inevitably afford him greater safety in the water.

Conformance to Rule.—In supervised and well-regulated bathing places, custom and knowledge of local conditions usually bring about the establishment of a set of regulations to govern the conduct of bathers. These rules follow quite normally a course beginning with the control of health factors by means of the required soap bath, the restriction of bathers who are unwell or suffering from infections and, frequently (generally in indoor natatoria) a physical examination by a physician as a preliminary requirement to bathing. Under certain conditions due to congestion of bathers regulations are in force to govern conduct on the beach or at the pool side. These, for example, may restrict ball playing among sun bathers on the beach or prohibit running and playing tag on the wet decks surrounding a pool and are established for the prevention of accidents by collision or from falls. Safe limits are established for bathing and are designated for the safety of the majority. All such rules are devised for the safety of the individual and the group by eliminating dangerous practices and bathers should conform to such regulations for the good of all even though they may seem to be individually irksome and unnecessarily restrictive at times.

There are, however, some possibilities of accident in bathing despite observance of rules governing personal conduct. They arise from the unforeseen circumstance and require some special knowledge of conditions and adaptation of skills to the unusual situation. Fortunately these conditions are well known and methods of combating them have been quite carefully worked out.

Currents.—Such currents, caused by flowing movements of water, as set out from land are an ever present source of danger to river and open water bathers since they tend to carry the bather away from the shore, often before he is aware of what is taking place. In rivers these currents are most deceptive. They rarely follow the contour of the river bed, even in comparatively straight stretches. Governed by projecting headlands, back waters, islands and the windings of its course, the direction of its flow wanders from shore to shore, now toward and then away from it. For every in-setting current there is sure to be an out-setting one nearby.

In the ocean, two kinds of currents are menacing to bathers, those caused by the tides and those caused by the run back of large waves from a beach. The first are known variously as along-shore currents, run-outs and sloughs and the latter are known as undertows. Tide currents move large masses of water, as a rule, and may run for considerable distances. Undertows, on the other hand, are merely the receding movements of water piled up by wave action on a shelving shore which, following the incline of the beach, run back under oncoming waves. While an undertow is sometimes quite violent it runs but a short distance.

Other current conditions are found at the confluence of large rivers or at the mouths of rivers emptying into the sea where the opposing forces of currents, or of currents and tides create what has been called a "jobble" of water, a maze of conflicting currents and waves, but since such places because of the roughness of the water are not inviting to the swimmer and are seldom used for bathing, they will not be dealt with further.

There is one fundamental principle which governs the safety of a swimmer caught in a current and that is, never to "buck" it. If the current has any considerable strength, even the strongest swimming effort cannot be very effective in stemming it for very long. Even a very good swimmer swims less than three miles an hour and currents frequently run from four to six. One should always swim diagonally across a current and with its flow, even though it may mean that the swimmer will come to land some distance from the point where he entered the water. This is true particularly of river and tidewater bathing where the currents run along shore. When the set of the current is directly outward from an open shore, the swimmer caught and unable to regain the beach should conserve his strength by drifting with it and shout or wave an arm occasionally to summon assistance from shore. While the pull of an undertow is short, it differs from other currents in that it runs deeper as it goes outward. The swimmer caught in an undertow should turn, go with it and take a diagonal course to the surface.

Weeds.—Water weed and eel grass are commonly found at or near swimming places, particularly in shallow ponds and streams and in tidewater rivers, salt water lagoons and shallow bays. These do not constitute a serious menace to the swimmer if, when he comes in contact with them, he does not try convulsively to thrash his way clear. Quick sharp movements only tend to wrap the weeds and grass securely about the legs and arms and hold the swimmer fast. Slow gentle drawing and shaking movements of the limbs will serve to clear them, even though the first convulsive reaction at contact has bound the swimmer tightly. If there is a current, one should always go with it, remembering that it will help to untangle and loosen the binding grass or weed. If the swimmer dives into masses of weed and is held under water, he must carefully estimate the length of time he can stay under and work with as much speed as he can, consistent with the necessity for making gentle movements.

Cramp.—Cramp has been called the bane of swimming since it causes pain and discomfort, and engenders panic and fright in the swimmer's mind and many times results in a drowning. Cramp occurs in muscles, making in the belly of the muscle a tight hard knot which for the time being incapacitates the part of the body in which it occurs, or, at least, greatly inhibits its action. It is accompanied always by pain in greater or lesser degree, depending upon its location. Cold or tired muscles are most susceptible and as the muscles of a swimmer frequently may be in this condition, cramp is of common occurrence while bathing. The parts most often affected by cramp when swimming are the foot, the calf of the leg and the hand. Cramp may also occur in the back of the thigh and, rarely, in the upper arm. In all such cases, the treatment is the same. The swimmer

Fig. 2. Releasing cramp in foot.

Fig. 3. Kneading out cramp in leg.

Fig. 4. Effect of stomach cramp.

rolls to a face down position in the water, with lungs fully inflated and grasps the cramped area firmly with one or both hands. Continued pressure will release the cramp but if the part is cold, vigorous kneading must be resorted to, to restore circulation, otherwise the cramp is likely to recur.

When cramp attacks the stomach or abdomen, the situation is much more serious since if the swimmer does not receive aid, he will, in all likelihood, drown. Stomach cramp, as before stated, is not an uncommon result of swimming too soon after eating but what muscles are affected is not known. All that is known is that the sudden attack is accompanied by such pain that quite involuntarily the knees are drawn to the chest as the head is drawn down and forward. Breathing is inhibited, as it is by a "stitch" in the side or back, and, apparently, no controlled movements can be made. Under such circumstances there is little that the victim can do to help himself and he must rely upon someone else to bring him to safety.

Disrobing.—When a person is precipitated fully clad into deep water, it is obvious that movement will be so hampered by the drag of water-soaked garments that he will soon become exhausted. The clothing, therefore, should be removed at once. To do this easily and with a minimum of effort expended the swimmer should inflate the lungs and submerge to a turtle floating position with arms and legs hanging directly downward. Using both hands, he should loosen and take off the shoes. This may take several breaths to accomplish. After the shoes are removed the same process, in the same position, should be used to take off the trousers or skirt and lastly, the coat or shirt should be removed. If the upper or outer garment, because of its design, has to come off over the head, it should be gathered up to the armpits; then, by seizing the bunched garment on both sides, with crossed arms, the swimmer can submerge and draw the garment up over the head, using one hand to free the back of the head, if necessary. When the body and head are freed, the swimmer removes the arms from the sleeves and swims clear.

Fig. 5. Disrobing. Removing shoe.

Fig. 6. Disrobing. Taking off shirt.

Fig. 7. Disrobing. Removing one-piece dress.

Capacity for Rescuing Others.—The blind instinct to give assistance to a person in danger of drowning is innate in many people and prompts them often to deeds of heroism in attempting rescues for which they are poorly or not at all fitted. The tale of needless sacrifice in the history of swimming is a long one wherein the heroism displayed has availed nothing. The parent, quite unable to swim, displays most frequently the blind courage which prompts him or her to rush to the aid of the child; to flounder into deep water where that child is in difficulty only to become a second victim and perish. Brothers and sisters, friends, even total strangers, often behave similarly with tragic consequences. Nor is this instinct to aid limited to non-swimmers. Novices and even very good swimmers frequently find that their ability to make a rescue does not equal their good intent and they either break away from the clutches of the drowning person with great difficulty or drown with him. In their desire to aid they so frequently ignore perfectly safe means of effecting a rescue which are conveniently at hand and plunge blindly ahead to attempt the rescue in the most perilous fashion —this is the tragedy.

Anyone who has even the slightest interest in aquatics should know the kind of rescue for which he is fitted; further than that, he should be able to size up a situation and use the best and safest means of helping the unfortunate victim, if he is to preserve his own life. Everyone has the capacity to aid in some fashion no matter what the degree of his aquatic skill or lack of it may be and he should learn and practice the forms of rescue suited to his abilities. Furthermore, as his aquatic skill advances to ever higher levels, he should parallel this development with the practice of life saving skills commensurate with his steadily increasing water ability. Finally, no one should employ the more spectacular forms of rescue, if less perilous methods may be used just as effectively.

Sinclair and Henry in their book on Swimming published as a volume of the Badminton Library in 1894 recount a tale of heroism which aptly proves a point. The tale is much too long to be quoted in full here but in substance it is this: A boat load of mill workers were being ferried across the Clyde one evening. The boat was badly overloaded and had not proceeded twenty yards from the dock, when it listed suddenly and overturned. One James Lambert, a powerful swimmer by the record and a good waterman, found himself in the water gripped about by as many men and women as could lay hands on him while others held to them. With marvelous self-possession and cold courage he allowed himself to sink to the bottom with his burden and found the water to be about ten feet deep. Being quite unable to swim because of the manner in which he was held he, nevertheless, contrived to get his feet down and shove diagonally to the surface and some few feet toward the dock before he sank again. Thus alternately driving off the bottom, getting a breath of air and sinking again he managed to near the dock where ropes and boathooks were used to relieve him of his burden. Upon checking it was found that he had brought in sixteen or seventeen of the unfortunates but he did not rest there. Plunging in again and yet once more he brought to shore first, two girls and then another girl and her young man, who were drowning together. Then, and this is the irony of it, he found himself clinging to the quay so spent that he would inevitably have sunk and drowned if an old and decrepit man had not seen him and, extending his cane to him, towed him along the quay to shallow water and helped him out. Thus the most spectacular rescue of all time would have ended tragically for the hero, if the old man had not used effectively, if not as spectacularly, the only means at hand commensurate with his strength and ability. The story points its own moral.

CHAPTER II

BATHING PLACES

Obviously one of the first principles of safe bathing is to choose a safe place in which to bathe. A reasonably safe place is one in which hazard is reduced to a minimum, provision made as far as possible for the prevention of accidents, and proper supervision and suitable equipment provided for the detection and rescue of those who get into difficulty. Beyond this it is not possible to go. Only a small proportion of the many thousands of bathing places in this country, however, even approach such a standard for safety and many of the places at which people customarily bathe do not meet even one requirement for water safety.

Swimming holes in abandoned quarries and small streams, or at points along rivers generally in the vicinity of cities and towns, are the most dangerous bathing places in the country and they number thousands. Often the water is of poor quality and pollution is not uncommon. They are far from attractive in many cases and bathers frequent them not from choice but because they want to swim and there are no better places available. The swimming hole is frequented usually by small boys from the poorer and less-privileged sections of towns and cities. There they seek diversion, comfort and enjoyment during hot weather under dangerous conditions and no supervision. There is no formal instruction so most of those who learn how to swim are self-taught or learn by imitation and in the trial and error process of learning some, inevitably, drown.

Fig. 8. The old swimming hole is usually dangerous.

Miles of less frequented sea beaches and shores of lakes and ponds fail to meet any of the standards of safety deemed adequate for bathers. There, however, the responsibility in case of water accident rests with the individual bather who chooses to bathe despite unsafe conditions of which he should be aware.

Established bathing beaches and indoor and outdoor pools more nearly meet the standards of supervision and equipment necessary for safe bathing but even here there are grave deficiencies in many places which menace the lives and safety of bathers. It is gratifying to note, however, the increasing number of bathing beaches and pools which set and meet the highest standards of safety in selection of site, of construction, in supervision and in equipment. The fact, however, that so much bathing is done in unsupervised and unequipped waters puts the burden of responsibility in the last analysis upon the individual himself and calls for the exercise of good judgment and foreknowledge of where and under what conditions he may bathe safely.

Common Safety Factors for Bathing Places

There are some safety factors for the prevention of drowning and accidents other than drowning in and about the bathing area, which are common to all bathing places.

Good Bottom.—In all places other than artificial pools a good bottom is one that slopes gently toward deep water with no holes, sudden step-offs or hidden obstructions such as large rocks, stumps, snags and sunken logs. The bottom should be composed of firm sand, gravel or shale, at least in standing depth areas and should have no silt, quicksand, shell patches, sharp and broken rock or debris on the bottom. Often bad conditions may be corrected where the site is otherwise suitable by removing boulders, stumps and logs or marking those which cannot be moved. Deposits of silt up to six or eight inches in depth on firm gravel bottom may be cleared by actual use. (Note: Silt thus broken up and suspended in the water will be washed outward to deep water, gradually leaving a clean bottom.) Shell, sharp stone, and debris such as broken glass, old tin cans and junk may be removed by raking.

The bottom of artificial pools should incline gradually toward the deep end or side and should be surfaced with smooth cement finish or unglazed tile. Rough cement is responsible for a great many scraped and cut feet which may become infected. Glazed tile offers treacherous footing causing many a nonswimmer to lose his balance and get into trouble.

Safe Beaches, Runways and Decks.—Beaches should be of sand or gravel and must be kept clean and well raked at all times. No picnicking should be allowed on the

Fig. 9. An attractive and well-planned swimming area at a summer camp.

beach paralleling the swimming area and under no conditions should glass or tin containers for food or drink be permitted on the beach. Runways, docks and floats should be of sturdy construction and placed low enough especially over shallow water, so that jumping from them will not cause injury. Ladders should be provided at frequent intervals along the faces of docks or floats in deep water to enable bathers to gain safety. Runways and docks should be cross-planked and laid with open seams for good drainage. Planking laid lengthwise, when wet, presents one of the most common causes of falls. The decks of floats should always be covered with heavy canvas, cocoa matting or painted, and sanded while the paint is still wet, to afford secure footing.

The decks and runways surrounding artificial pools or tanks should be finished with a semi-smooth surface of cement or unglazed tile. Strips of corrugated rubber should not be used as water collecting beneath them creates an unsanitary condition. The same may be said of unsightly duck-boards.

Swimming Areas.—Swimming areas for various classifications of bathers should be clearly defined or marked. Indoor and outdoor tanks of standard sizes definitely limit bathing by their size and markings. They have, as a rule, a gradually deepening shallow end for non-swimmers and the remainder of the pool is given over to swimmers and divers. In inset tile or painted letters they should always bear the marking, "Shallow End," "Deep End," as the case may be. They should also have maximum and minimum depths indicated in the same way.

Swimming beaches and semi-artificial outdoor pools should have the areas for various classifications of bathers clearly defined by buoyed lines or booms. If not indicated by the natural contour of the bathing area, the non-swimmers section should be marked.

Fig. 10. Small craft operation away from swimming area.

Small Craft in Bathing Areas.—No craft other than lifeboats should be allowed in the swimming area. Buoys indicating the outermost limits of the area should be placed at regular intervals and bear a warning to all craft to keep out. Especially must motor boat operators be warned against driving among swimmers. The high speeds at which unguarded propellers turn offer a serious menace to life and limb of bathers.

Cribs.—It is not always possible to find ideal conditions for bathing beaches. The water may be excellent at some points and offer inviting inducement to swimmers but because of the lack of shallow water, or a poor bottom it cannot be used by non-swimmers and beginners. This handicap may be overcome by constructing a crib. A beginner's crib is essentially an open-seamed scow made of planks which when placed in the water fills but remains afloat. It is rectangular in shape and may be of a size which will permit stroke practice for numbers of beginners without crowding. A good size for the average bathing place is twenty feet by thirty feet. Its depth should be not less than three and not more than four feet. Runways three feet in width are constructed around its edges with a stout rail on the outer side where it overhangs the water. Beneath the runways are placed watertight oil drums or casks in sufficient number to give the required buoyancy to the structure. The inside surface of the planking should be painted and sanded to afford secure footing and even so it must be scrubbed periodically with a stiff brush to rid it of slime and algae. Frequent inspections are necessary to check for splinters and projecting nails, spikes and bolts. The crib is moored as close to shore as possible and connected to it by a runway. The crib should never be too commodious or too attractive since its only purpose is to afford non-swimmers a chance to learn how to swim. As soon as some skill is acquired, they should do their swimming in deep water. Cribs are unwieldly structures and cannot be placed securely on open shores of large bodies of water where they will be subject to the action of wind and wave, as the pounding they receive will soon render them unfit for service. In northern latitudes they cannot be left in the water through the winter because of the destructive action of ice. They must be hauled up on shore above high water level in the autumn and put in again in the spring. This automatically limits them in size and makes very stout construction necessary.

Offshore Floats.—Wherever possible all structures for diving and sun decks should be a part of the dock system of the waterfront, but where a bathing beach has areas of shallow water which extend out a considerable distance, it is not always wise or feasible to extend the dock system far enough out to get deep water for diving. Under these circumstances the float anchored offshore or the diving platform erected on a sub-surface structure solidly placed on the bottom solves the problem. It is rarely justifiable to place them so close to water of standing depth as to offer a constant challenge to the novice swimmer. Probably the greatest number of near-drowning accidents at public bathing places occur between the shallow area and the offshore float. Under no conditions should life lines attached to the float extend inward to the shallow area. Some non-swimmers will inevitably try to follow the lines hand-over-hand out to the float and if they lose the hold in deep water or if the lines sag beneath the surface they will get into difficulty.

Diving Structures.—Diving, except plain headers for entering the water, should be restricted to structures and areas provided for the purpose. Indiscriminate diving into swimming areas has been the source of serious injury to numbers of unsuspecting swimmers as well as to the divers themselves.

Diving platforms upon which springboards are erected and diving towers should be of strong construction and put together

Fig. 11. An unusually large dock system in use.

with galvanized iron bolts rather than spikes because the constant vibration of springboards in use will loosen timbers and draw nails or spikes.

Springboards and diving towers should be erected according to the recommendations made in the A.A.U. or Intercollegiate rule book for Swimming and Diving. Springboards for real safety should always be almost level from base to tip and project well out over the water. A springboard should not rise from butt to tip more than two inches in its length. For low springboards up to one meter in height above the surface of the water, water eight feet deep is the minimum requirement for safety. Springboards placed at three meters (approximately ten feet) require ten feet of water and diving towers above this height, not less than fifteen feet. No two springboards or spring-board and tower should be placed so that they have the same point of entry. The points at which divers enter the water should be at least ten feet from each other. This precludes the danger-ous practice of erecting a high board directly over a low one, or a diving tower above a springboard. The danger of divers col-liding in the air or at the surface of the water makes this safety requirement apparent. All boards and tower platforms should be covered with cocoa matting or similar material to afford sure footing.

Ladders must be provided at frequent intervals along the dock or pool face to enable divers to regain the platform or deck.

Supervision of Bathers.—Every organized bathing beach or swimming pool requires supervision of the bathers by men or women well-trained to control activities and to act intelligently and correctly in an emergency. These may be instructors, paid life guards, volunteer trained life savers who, out of regard for others, supervise bathing without re-muneration, or merely trained life savers who mingle with the bathers.

Life guards on bathing beaches which are frequented by large numbers of bathers must isolate themselves on stands from which they can keep a constant watch over the bathers. They may occupy lifeboats patrolling the outer limits of the bathing area or they may cover a section of the beach on foot. During hours on duty they never enter the water themselves ex-cept to assist someone in difficulty. On bathing beaches of small-er proportions and at swimming pools, an instructor or guard should be on duty at all times during bathing hours and should practice the same watchful attentiveness employed on the larger beaches.

If the supervisor of any bathing place is a qualified Life

Fig. 12. Life guard tower on surf beach.

Saving examiner he may, if the beach or pool is undermanned for reasonable safety, select, train and qualify as life savers certain of the better swimmers who swim habitually at his beach or in his pool. When fully trained and adjudged competent, they may be used as volunteer assistants to help him in supervising and patrolling the bathing place.

Trained and qualified junior and senior life savers among the bathers at any beach or pool add an excellent safety factor to that place since they are bathers themselves mingling with the others and are always ready to give assistance in time of need.

Regulation of Bathers for Safety.—No bathing place can be considered a safe one unless the activities of its patrons are regulated. Manifestly hazardous acts must be prohibited. Swimmers, no matter how skilled they are, must be restrained from swimming beyond the supervised area unless they clearly understand that they go on their own responsibility. Non-swimmers must stay in shallow water and be prevented from venturing into deep water trusting to the support of a swimmer, water wings or an inflated tube. Novice divers must be constrained from attempting fancy diving skills for which they are not yet ready because of lack of experience and if there is a high platform for diving it should not be used by the incompetent. Play activities on the beach, on docks or decks of pools and in shallow water should be confined to certain areas and to games which will not endanger either the participants or bystanders. Horseplay must not be tolerated. Regulations for the control of bathers should be as simple and as few in number as possible. If established by custom and enforced with tact, they will not prove to be unduly irksome to the average bather. As a matter of fact all but a small minority of bathers regulate their own water activities and keep them within limits set by their known level of skill. When they get into difficulty it is almost always due to ignorance of conditions. It is the small minority of bathers who are foolhardy, indifferent to the rights of others and lacking in good judgment. It is fortunate, indeed, that this group is small for if in the majority it would scarcely be possible to control the huge crowds which gather at some of our larger bathing beaches in the summer time, and the resultant loss of life would be much greater than it is at present.

Equipment for Safety and Rescue

Certain equipment for self-rescue and rescue by others is a vital requirement for water accident prevention at any bathing place. Not all of the equipment listed here is necessary for every bathing beach or pool, of course. Specific rescue equipment for various types of bathing places will be given subsequently.

Life Lines.—These are stretched or buoyed lines which mark bathing area limits. If properly rigged they afford temporary support to the tired swimmer or to one who is struggling in a current.

Booms.—Booms made of good sized logs chained together are often used to enclose a whole swimming area, especially in streams or rivers. These offer support or protection at any point in their length.

Resting Floats or Buoys.—Small floats about three feet square or spherical watertight buoys, anchored at intervals in the deep water portion of the swimming area afford resting places for tired swimmers. While not large enough to climb on, they offer a handhold to which the swimmer may hang while he recovers breath and strength. They should be equipped with life lines looped about them close enough to the surface so that little effort need be expended in securing and maintaining the grasp.

Lifeboat.—A lifeboat is a seaworthy yet reasonably light and handy rowboat which is held always in readiness and fully equipped to assist or rescue persons in danger of drowning. It may be drawn upon the beach just above the water line, moored to a dock or manned by a trained life saver on the outer edges of the bathing area. Depending upon conditions it may be handled by a single oarsman and a boat steerer, or two oarsmen and a boat steerer. The lifeboat should be equipped with the following:

1. The required number of oars for the crew.
2. Spare oars.
3. A light bamboo pole about ten feet long.
4. A ring buoy with line attached (not necessary in some instances).
5. A bailer.
6. An anchor.

Fig. 13. A type of life boat.

Surfboard.—The light surfboard is another type of rescue apparatus which has great value for rescue especially on open beaches or at bathing places of considerable area. During bathing hours it is placed near the water where it may be launched very quickly to proceed to the rescue.

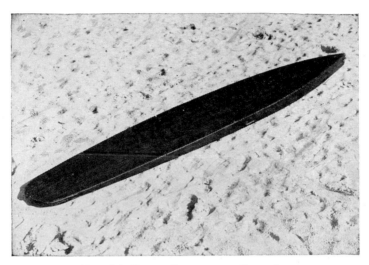

Fig. 14. Type of rescue surfboard.

Heaving Lines.—The heaving line is a very inexpensive rescue device which has real value at a waterfront particularly around the docks. It is merely a sixty foot length of quarter or three-eighths inch line the end of which is fashioned into a large knot such as the "monkey-fist." Several of these lines coiled and hung in readiness for service may be placed at strategic points on the docks where one may be seized and hurled to a person in danger of drowning. While the line does not float and cannot be cast as far as a ring buoy, by casting half the coils and allowing the remainder to feed off the other hand, it can be thrown with reasonable accuracy and is good for a range of forty to fifty feet.

Pole and Shepherd's Crook.—For making rescues close to safety, especially off docks, in swimming pools and from lifeboats, the light bamboo pole from ten to fifteen feet in length is an excellent device as one end can be thrust into the hands of the drowning person and he can be drawn to safety. The shepherd's crook is a long light pole with a blunted hook large enough to encircle the victim's body. It may be placed in a rack at a point where it is likely to be needed. With it, a person may be grappled and hauled to safety even though unconscious or so weak from exhaustion that he cannot hold on.

The Ring Buoy.—The light casting ring buoy is considered almost standard equipment for pools and bathing beaches where it may be thrown to persons in difficulty near the shore or side. The standard throwing buoy is fifteen inches in diameter, weighs two and a half pounds and is fitted with sixty feet of one-quarter inch line. Placed on racks convenient to points where they are likely to be used, ring buoys constitute an ever ready means of giving aid.

Swimming Rescue Buoys.—This type of buoy was designed to be towed out to a victim by a swimming rescuer. Primarily it was devised for making rescues in surf where it could serve as a support for one or more persons, but its use has become widespread for rescue in any open waters.

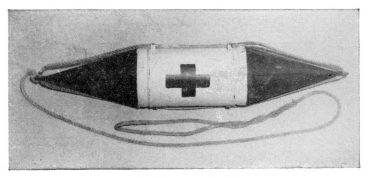

Fig. 15. The torpedo buoy.

This buoy varies in shape and in material used in its construction and it bears a variety of names. It is made of metal, rubber or balsa wood and, according to its shape, is known as the diamond, torpedo or can buoy.

Grappling Irons.—Grappling irons should be considered not only as body recovery but as rescue devices, since the first few casts of the irons may bring a victim to the surface in water too deep for diving and in time to use artificial respiration successfully. While grappling irons should never be placed where they are exposed to public view, they should be kept fully-rigged and ready for use in a locker close to the waterfront where they are easily accessible and can be put into operation with little delay.

The Water Scope.—The water scope or water glass as it is sometimes known is useful only in places where the water is reasonably clear. There it is used for scanning the bottom either from dock, float or boat to locate a submerged victim.

First Aid Equipment.—Large bathing beaches are usually equipped with an Emergency First Aid room where injuries are cared for and after treatment for submersion given. They may have trained nurses in attendance and, in some cases, a doctor. Not all bathing beaches or pools can be so serviced but a minimum requirement for any organized waterfront or pool should be a First Aid kit of sufficient size for anticipated needs and at least one trained First Aider to use its contents. The First Aid kit should be within easy access to meet emergencies at the scene of injury. A pocket kit is sufficient for First Aid treatment of small cuts and bruises.

Types of Bathing Places

The "Swimming Hole."—Because of its association with youth and carefree summer days, the "old swimming hole" has become in the public mind the most romantic of swimming places. A deep pool in a small stream, a sandbar, a break in the undergrowth on the shore of pond or lake, an abandoned quarry, even a pier head; these and many others multiplied a thousand times have in the past and are today the scene of the early aquatic exploits of tens of thousands of children. In such places there is and always has been freedom of action, pleasure, physical and mental exuberance, even if there has been little safety. Despite increased pollution of streams and the provision of better swimming facilities it is idle to suppose that the swimming hole will be entirely eliminated. Thousands of such places will still serve many people for bathing especially in rural areas. Indeed, as larger and larger areas of sub-marginal land are taken over by State and Federal governments for park purposes the number may even increase. If only a little attention is given to the elimination of hazards and the safeguarding of those who bathe, much of the danger can be eliminated and bathing in the swimming hole may be not only a pleasant experience but a reasonably safe one.

Swimming holes are not selected haphazardly as a rule. They are chosen usually because they offer some of the following advantages: a beach, an area of shallow water, deep water, rocks, overhanging banks or a bridge for diving. Numbered among their chief hazards may be swift currents, step-offs, submerged rocks, stumps and snags, water too shallow for safe diving or water too deep for non-swimmers and learners. In addition, they can offer no trained supervision. To offset these conditions, a number of things may be done.

Frequenting almost any swimming hole are a few highly skilled boy swimmers who are termed in some parts of the country "water rats." This name betokens admiration for a degree of "at homeness" in the water which is somewhat akin to the aquatic abilities of the muskrat. These boys with a little proper training may learn Life Saving readily and qualify as Junior or even Senior Life Savers. This they may do through Scouting, 4-H Club work or any other of a dozen youth organizations which incorporate swimming and life saving training in their program. It may even be that training can be secured in their school physical education program. A few trained life savers in every swimming hole group will always be the best safeguard against drowning accidents. If there is added to this just a few homely safeguards, the swimming hole can be made a reasonably safe place to bathe.

Where necessary, the shallow water area can be enclosed by a boom of logs. A few logs roped end to end and flung around the area or marking its outside limit, will indicate to non-swimmers how far they may venture. All submerged rocks, snags and waterlogged timbers which constitute a menace and which cannot be removed can be marked by sticks thrust upright near them or by small floating buoys made of bits of timber, anchored above them. Springboards should be placed only where the water is deep enough for safe diving and mounted securely and correctly. One or two poles some ten or twelve feet long, which may be cut in the woods, can be placed conveniently on the banks where they can be used for reaching rescues. A coil of line hung where it can be put into use quickly may be the means of saving a person's life with no risk to the rescuer.

If the swimming holes of the country are thus made safe by those who use them habitually a great reduction in the loss of life by drowning will result.

Unsupervised Bathing Beaches.—Long stretches of shoreline of ponds, lakes and sea in this country are wholly unorganized and unsupervised for bathing. This may be due to the fact that they are little used or because they are located at some distance from centers of population or vacation colonies. Little can be done to safeguard bathers under these conditions. Established life guards are not practicable and any safety equipment which may be placed at such places is liable to be stolen or maliciously destroyed. The bather must, therefore, find the means of safeguarding his life within himself or within his group. If he is a non-swimmer, he will confine his bathing to shallow and safe waters. If he is a swimmer, he will do his swimming in reasonable proximity to shore and take no chances. Non-swimmer or swimmer, he will never bathe alone. He will do his bathing with a partner who at least, can swim and preferably one skilled in life saving. Picnic and outing parties should number among their members one or more trained life savers if they intend to do any bathing and the place should always be selected with care and conditions of water and bottom quickly ascertained. Only in this way will unorganized bathing in unsupervised waters be somewhat safe.

Organized Bathing Beaches.—An organized bathing beach is a section of shoreline on which control of bathers is exercised by trained personnel, supervision offered and means of rescue afforded. This may be a hundred feet of beach on a small pond or stream, five miles of seashore, or anything in between. It may accommodate a hundred bathers or one hundred thousand, but the problem of safety is the same varying only in degree and amount of control and supervision necessary.

Life guards or bathing supervisors are essential. These not only are trained to make rescues but to control bathing as well. The number of guards required varies. One guard may be able to supervise effectively the bathing activities of a hundred persons provided they are concentrated in an area which he can cover quickly and easily. If the situation is complicated by having not only a swimming area but a diving section and an offshore float as well, one man can hardly take care of the three sections adequately.

Where concentration of bathers is heavy, particularly at surf bathing beaches, one guard stationed in a tower is needed for every hundred yards of beach and a guard in a boat patrolling the outer fringe of bathers is needed for every two hundred yards of shoreline. On Saturdays, Sundays and holidays it is often necessary to double the force of guards to prevent loss of life. Frequently, regular bathers who have had training in life saving form a volunteer auxiliary body to aid regular life guards on such days. Extra guards are needed at diving piers and on or near offshore floats.

Restricted areas for various classifications of bathers, life lines where needed and resting floats are devices for general safety which are widely used on many beaches. (Resting floats are not practical for open beaches on large bodies of water where heavy surf may tear them loose from their moorings.)

Lifeboats, surfboards, ring buoys, torpedo buoys and grappling irons, in sufficient quantity for all needs, are essential to the safe bathing beach. Open surf beaches do not require ring buoys but otherwise the above equipment is standard.

A near-drowning at a congested bathing beach must be handled as unobtrusively as possible. There should be no concentration of guards at the point where a rescue is being made, no warning whistles or sirens (except at some surf bathing beaches where they are necessary to summon assistance), no delay in effecting the rescue and moving the victim to the bathhouse or emergency room where he may be treated for submersion unless artificial respiration is indicated. It is no uncommon thing for a wave of hysteria to sweep through a congested mass of bathers when they become aware that someone is drowning and for a half dozen others to get into difficulty immediately as a result of fear. Therefore, instead of rushing to assist in the rescue of the initial victim, life guards other than those at the rescue point hold their stations and redouble their vigilance over the sectors for which they are responsible.

Life guards from their towers and boats survey a scene of constant activity. It is nothing short of marvelous to the uninitiated to see how unerringly the life guard can pick out the person in difficulty from the thousands before him and proceed to his assistance. The answer is simple. The good life guard has trained his eyes to see only the unnatural in the constantly changing scene before him. The natural movements of swimming, bathing, diving and jumping which he has noted thousands of times in his experience, his trained eye passes over. It is the unnatural movement or position of a person in distress or the agitated demeanor of nearby bathers which catches his eye immediately. Rarely does he need a cry for help to attract his attention. Usually he is on his way out long before someone thinks to shout.

The head life guard on a surf beach is generally a person of long experience. He knows the beach and the water conditions thereon as an average person knows his home. He knows where it is safe to bathe and when and if he closes one section or all of the beach to bathers, his dictates should be accepted without question even though it debars some fine and fearless swimmers from enjoyment. He knows when the undertow is bad and where and when run-outs are making. He may not be concerned about the ability of the good swimmer to take care of himself but he knows that if he lets one go in others less capable will follow, and then he will have his hands full hauling them to safety. The restraint placed upon a good swimmer from going too far out on any bathing beach is not so much for the safety of that swimmer as it is for other and poorer swimmers who try to emulate his feats.

A well-supervised bathing beach under the control of a sufficient number of life guards properly trained and adequately equipped is one of the safest places to bathe. There are beaches on our seaboard where natural water conditions are not always good, where thousands of bathers enjoy themselves day after day through the summer months, at which no drownings have occurred for a period of from five to seven years. This fine record is no happy circumstance but is, rather, the result of excellent control of bathers and a high standard of efficiency in life saving.

The Swimming Pool or Tank.—Outdoor artificial pools of large area are safeguarded in essentially the same manner as supervised bathing beaches, even to lifeboats. Such pools are usually semi-natural in design; that is, water is impounded in a natural depression in the terrain which by excavation, damming or diking has been made suitable for bathing. Some are filled from artesian wells, some by streams while others (on the sea coast) admit and hold tidal water. Artificial pools of this character generally have sand bottoms and earth banks and the water is not filtered, thus practically all the conditions of a natural waterfront are to be found there.

Pools or tanks which are wholly artificial in type and construction, whether indoor or in the open, present fewer problems connected with the safety of the bathers and require much less rescue apparatus than the large pool or bathing beach. Water accident prevention, therefore, is more a matter of regulation and control of bathers than it is of rescue. The dimensions of the tank are not large. Indoors they are standardized in lengths of twenty yards, twenty-five yards or twenty-five meters and their width rarely exceeds forty-two feet; a few are somewhat larger. Out-of-doors, artificial tanks may run larger but they are very much smaller in area than most natural bathing places. At no place in the tank is the bather very far from a side or an end.

Artificial swimming pools must be supervised during all bathing hours. At all other times they should be closed to bathers by locking doors or gates. Poles and shepherd's crooks are the chief rescue devices of standard size indoor pools; with them any part of the pool may be reached. For larger pools with high ceilings and for those located in the open, ring buoys and lines are of considerable value. Organization of bathers for safety is not necessary in filtered or clear water tanks of average dimensions but where the water is not clear enough to see the bottom in all parts of the pool, the Buddy system may be employed to good advantage.

Unsafe practices must be eliminated from the outset. Diving from balconies or rafters, playing tag on the deck and runways around the pool, diving haphazardly among swimmers, wrestling, and pushing unsuspecting individuals into the water are some of the things which cannot be tolerated. Serious and painful injuries have often been caused by thoughtless actions of this character.

Methods of Safety Organization within Bathing Groups

At public bathing places organization for safety among the bathers themselves is rarely, if ever, possible. At swimming holes and on unsupervised beaches the safety of the bather lies largely in responsibility for his own individual actions and to a much lesser extent upon those with whom he bathes. On supervised beaches and in pools, the responsibility is first, individual, and second, that of the supervisor or life guard. Individual members of the group, as a rule, are too unrelated in abilities, interests and relationships to permit of organization by which they are made responsible for each other. Lack of concentration of bathers also makes any system of checking individuals in and out of the water impracticable. It is only among organized groups of bathers where control can be exercised over every member that any system can be made actually workable which makes individuals responsible for individuals within the group and permits the supervisor to check every member in and out of the water. Thus, children and even adults, in organized camps, in swimming classes, at bathing beaches and pools, on bathing parties, picnics, hikes and so on, can use protective systems by which greater safety for every member is assured.

Checking Systems.—In organized group bathing in the open, some system of checking bathers in and out of the water should be employed as a means of preventing the harrowing experience of having some member of the group disappear beneath the surface and have his loss go undiscovered for some time after the bathing period is over.

Real safety for group bathing requires competent supervision in the ratio of at least one supervisor to every ten bathers. In addition, some means must be employed by which every member of the group entering the water is known to have come out again at the end of the bathing period.

Roll Call.—Where the group of bathers is not so large as to make this system cumbersome, all bathers may be checked in and out simply by calling the roll from a prepared list of names. In well-organized camps where the same group bathes regularly day after day, each member may be given a number which can be checked expeditiously on a prepared list.

Check Boards.—A check board is a device by which the bather checks himself in and out of the water doing away with the necessity of calling the roll. Generally, it is a plane board surface studded with nails or hooks from which are hung tags of metal or cardboard, one for each person in the swimming group. On the tag is a number or the name of the person and frequently one side is colored red. In use, the bather turns his check over on the hook before entering the water and upon leaving turns it back again. At the end of the bathing period the supervisor of the waterfront can with a glance determine if all who entered the water have left it. If the reverse side of the tags is red, one glance will suffice to account for the bathers and if any one is apparently missing, search for him in the camp as well as in the water may be begun with no delay.

Caps.—In girls' organizations particularly, a system of using colored bathing caps for supervision and control of bathers while in the water is frequently employed. The bathing group is divided into three sections according to their respective swimming abilities. Thus non-swimmers wear one color of cap, the elementary swimmers another and the swimmers still another. While there is no uniformity in color designations, it is suggested that where this system is used, the non-swimmers wear red caps, the elementary swimmers yellow, and the swimmers green or blue. White caps should be used by swimming supervisors and life savers. This is easy to remember and the brighter colors bring into prominence the two classifications most likely to need control or assistance.

The Buddy System.—Of all the systems yet devised for the control of large or small groups of organized bathers, the Buddy plan has proved to be the most effective. Essentially, it is merely a system of pairing all bathers in the group according to their respective abilities and making each member of the pair responsible for the whereabouts of the other. If they are non-swimmers in shallow water, elementary swimmers or swimmers and divers, they always remain in close proximity to one another and always enter and leave the water together. Thus by the simple plan of mutual responsibility every member of the bathing group whether it numbers fifty or five thousand, is under direct supervision. Buddies are not responsible for the rescue of their partners in case of trouble but they can always make known any danger and bring the supervisor or a life guard on the run to assist or rescue the one in trouble.

Because in the happy excitement of bathing, especially in children's groups, some are likely to stray too far and forget their responsibility to their partners, a system of checking buddies is usefully employed. At intervals in the bathing period, generally about every ten minutes the head supervisor blows his whistle or rings a bell. At this signal all activity must cease and buddies must join their partners and raise clasped hands. A quick glance by the supervisor to note that all are paired and then on the whistle or bell, activity is resumed. At first, some bathers may find this system irksome and restraining but if paired properly accordng to abilities they soon realize its value and become conditioned to bathing in this manner.

CHAPTER III

PERSONAL SAFETY AND SELF RESCUE IN THE USE OF SMALL CRAFT

The term small craft is applied essentially to one- and two-place boats propelled by oars, all canoes, small outboard motorboats and small sailing craft. These are by far the most numerous on the waters of this country both inland and coastal and because they are of no great length or beam and have little weight they are less stable than craft of greater proportions. Because of their instability and since many unskilled persons use them they figure frequently as factors in drowning accidents. Some of these craft, notably canoes, bear the stigma "dangerous" in the minds of many people when, as a matter of fact, they may be actually safer to use than many larger boats, if they are properly handled by persons adequately fitted to use them. Small craft have little freeboard, i. e., the sides are low and since they are open or have very small decks fore and aft, they fill quickly and easily if the gunwale dips beneath the surface even for a brief moment. To offset this condition, while they may capsize, they will not sink because they are constructed of buoyant materials or have airlocks. Small craft are definitely limited by wind, water and handling conditions and are safe for the user only if they are kept within safe limits. By small boats are meant those craft which have no decks, are light of construction and propelled by one or two pairs of oars. This definition includes the well-known square-end punt, the skiff or sharpie, the dinghy, the jolly-boat or wherry, the steel-boat, the dory-skiff and the Adirondack guide boat (a rowing canoe). Small sailboats include the sailing dinghy and any other open or partly decked small boat which uses lee-boards or centerboard and carries no weight on the keel or no ballast.

Canoes may be open or partially decked and as a class include all types: the graceful high-ended canvas-covered craft in common use, the guide model, the racing canoe, the kayak, the sailing canoe and the sponson.

Any boat equipped with a motor, either inboard or out-board, which has no decks or is decked except for a cockpit and does not exceed a length of eighteen feet may also be clas-sified as a small craft.

All of these are of limited stability and may be rather easily capsized or filled and require of the user some swim-ming ability, skill in handling and knowledge of when and where they may be used safely.

Swimming Skill a Requirement for Safe Operation of Small Craft.—To be reasonably safe it is quite true that every-one who uses a small boat or a canoe should know how to swim well enough to take care of himself in case the craft capsizes or if he falls out. Since, however, the incidence of rowboat cap-sizing is small, especially of the more clumsy punt and flat-bottomed skiff models of some stability, it can be said that non-swimmers may use them if accompanied by a trained life saver, but then only reasonably close to shore and shelter. A person having little or no swimming skill should not venture into the lighter types of boats or into canoes, unless the conditions under which the craft is used are exceptionally safe.

Preliminary Swimming Test.—A good preliminary swimming test for safe boat and canoe operation which anyone can apply to himself is simply this: To right himself after pitching into the water and recover to the surface; to get rid of shoes and hampering outer clothing and then to stay afloat for five minutes by treading water, swimming with a minimum of progress in any direction and by floating, or resting in a floating position. In this way one can be reasonably certain that, if thrown out of a boat or canoe, he can right himself and return to the surface, get rid of clothing and stay afloat until he determines what he must do to extricate himself from the situation.

Training Essential to Proper Handling.—Small boats and canoes are designed essentially for use on inland waterways, small lakes and protected sections of coastal waters and of larger lakes. Ordinary types cannot stand the buffeting of heavy seas nor can they be handled well and safely when the wind is blowing a gale and the water is extremely rough. The degree of weather and water conditions under which they can be used is entirely dependent upon the skill, training and experience of the user. For the novice, actual instruction and conscientious practice in calm water is essential. As skill is developed, heavier water may be attempted until, through thorough and progressive development, the highly skilled boatman or canoeist can handle his craft safely under conditions which would be extremely perilous for the average person. The use of rowboats and canoes which are flat-bottomed and relatively wide in proportion to their length, thereby possessing greater stability than the narrower round-bottomed craft, will afford the novice the greatest degree of safety during his period of training. In the use of small motorboats, having either inboard or outboard motors, only those of small power and no great speed should be operated by the novice. Learners as a class should do their learning and practicing in any type of small craft, in still or gently flowing water, along shore and never alone. All handling and maneuvering should be of the most fundamental type; plain rowing or paddling, steering, launching, landing and so on.

As skill in operation is developed the boatman or canoeist may use lighter craft of less stability and venture further from shore. He may go alone, too, without fear of misadventure. In company with a skilled companion he may undertake considerable journeys, try more rapidly moving water and attempt to master more complicated and intricate maneuvers.

The highly skilled user of small craft has few limitations placed upon his activities. He may run "white" water or paddle in a running sea in a canoe, sail a small boat in a stiff breeze, or guide a high-powered fast little outboard motorboat with reasonable safety. Due to his increased experience, he may essay stunt skills which are quite beyond the average, but always he must work up to them progressively through skills which are less exacting and require less experience and ability.

Correct Handling a Prime Requisite in Small Craft Safety.—Proper handling of any small craft is absolutely necessary for reasonable safety. Correct use of oars and paddles, sheet and tiller, motor and rudder determine what the craft will do, where it will go and how it will behave. There is no substitute for this knowledge and it must be gained as rapidly as the ability of the user will permit. Under instruction, of course, but largely through practice, this knowledge is acquired and along with it, skill and judgment are developed, and the latter is by no means the least important factor in small craft handling.

The first safety factor in using a boat or canoe is to know how to enter and leave it correctly. In entering a small craft whether from dock or beach, the boat or canoe must first be steadied. The user then steps into the bottom directly over the keel; not on the gunwale, thwart or stern seat. As soon as the whole weight of the occupant is in the craft and balanced, the center of gravity is lowered by stooping and steadying one's self with a hand on either gunwale preparatory to moving to the desired position. Leaving a small craft just reverses the process

Fig. 16. Boarding a canoe, first step. Keep your body weight on the foot on the dock.

Fig. 17. Boarding a canoe, second step. Grasp both gunwales as you transfer your body weight to the foot in the canoe.

Fig. 18. Boarding a canoe, third step. Place other foot in the canoe and kneel down.

Fig. 19. Entering a canoe from shallow water.

Fig. 20. Entering a canoe from the rocky bank of a river.

of entering. The craft is laid alongside the dock or landing stage and steadied; the weight is kept low and the balanced position over the keel is maintained until the occupant sets one foot upon terra firma when the weight is transferred to that foot with no backward thrust of the other foot against the boat or canoe.

Fig. 21. Boarding a canoe at a beach or shallow-water shore; one man holds the end while the other boards.

Fig. 22. Boarding a canoe at a beach or shallow-water shore; second man boarding while first aboard controls the canoe with his paddle. This canoe has been launched stern first.

Correct Positions for Rowing and Paddling.—Rowboats are equipped with thwarts or seats upon which the occupants sit. These, if placed correctly, are several inches lower than the gunwales of the boat. The beam or width of the average rowboat is great enough to permit the rower to sit comfortably on a thwart without danger of overturning provided he centers his weight over the keel and moves if he has to, with deliberation. Modern canoes likewise are equipped with seats. This, unfortunately, is due to public demand born of ignorance of the mechanics of stability, and paddling efficiency in a canoe. These seats are usually only a couple of inches below the gunwales and to sit on them to paddle is dangerous. The point at which the weight of the occupant is supported is so high that the craft is actually made top heavy and any sudden movement, due to wind, water or the paddler himself, easily throws it out of balance and causes it to capsize or else pitches the paddler into the water. Especially is this true of the light, fast slim models with rounded bottoms. All seats should be removed from canoes and the thwarts properly relocated to serve as supports for paddling as well as for structural braces as in the original Indian craft. The paddler should then learn to paddle in a kneeling position

Fig. 23. Best and safest paddling position.

Fig. 24. Relief paddling position (one knee).

using a pad under the knee or knees and supporting a portion of his weight comfortably on or against a thwart. This position when properly taken is comfortable even for sustained cruising, induces an erect posture and increases paddling efficiency, and converts the hitherto "tippy" canoe into a dependable and serviceable craft.

Changing Position.—One of the chief causes of drowning accidents from rowboats and canoes involves exchanging

Fig. 25. Exchanging positions in a canoe safely.

Fig. 26. Alternate method of exchanging positions safely.

positions by the occupants. Rarely, if ever, is there any actual necessity for the change and since it definitely creates a dangerous situation it is to be avoided. For the beginner and the novice there is only one really safe way to change places in either a rowboat or a canoe and that is to land and shift positions at the water's edge. The thoroughly trained and experienced boatman or canoeist who has acquired the niceties of balance and is familiar with every action of his craft may, by means of a properly planned procedure, change places safely while afloat. In a boat he may move over to a sitting position on the rowing thwart beside the rower while keeping the boat trimmed and on an even keel, by balancing the weight of one occupant with that of another. The rower may then shift to another thwart or to the stern seat.

In a canoe, however, the process of changing positions is more complicated and until the beginner or novice has received definite training under safe conditions it should not be attempted while afloat in water more than waist deep. To change position the paddles are placed in the canoe, the bow paddler moves back on hands and knees to a low crouched position amidships of the canoe. The stern paddler then moves forward with one hand on each gunwale and straddles over his partner to take his place at the bow and when he is in position, the first paddler sits upright and slides back to his new position in the stern. Thus, the balance is maintained and the canoe rides steadily on an even keel.

Safe Loads for Small Craft.—Small rowboats and canoes have no great passenger carrying capacity. The average single thwart rowboat does well to carry the rower and a single passenger sitting in the stern seat. The average two thwart boat can usually carry two oarsmen and two passengers or a single oarsman and three passengers of adult weight. Some types of rowboats are much larger and can carry a greater load, and it is sometimes difficult to determine the danger point of loading. By and large, it can be said for this classification of larger boats that the craft is not overloaded if it has in calm water a minimum of six inches of free board; i. e., if the gunwales at their lowest point are that height above the surface when the boat is fully loaded. For a choppy sea rather more free board is required for safety. Usually, the capacity of a rowboat is predetermined by the number of persons it will seat comfortably on thwarts or seats.

Fig. 27. Safe load for a rowboat.

In calm water the capacity of the average canoe can be roughly determined by its length. (The length, in addition to the manufacturer's number, is stamped inside the canoe at the bow and stern on the end of the inside stem piece.) The fifteen foot model is essentially designed for use by one adult; sixteen foot, two adults; seventeen foot, three adults; and eighteen foot, four adults.

Any boat or canoe which is maneuvered and steered with more difficulty than usual, which tends to respond sluggishly to the steersman's efforts and which is hard to trim and keep in balance is overloaded no matter what the number of its occupants may be.

Nothing should be taken for granted with passengers. It should never be assumed that they know how to enter and leave, and dispose themselves in small craft. Boats and canoes should be steadied alongside the dock or landing stage by laying hold of the gunwale from the dock itself, not from the craft, by the oarsman or paddler. The passenger should be "handed" into the craft, being told where to step and where to sit. Only after all passengers are in and properly seated should the oarsmen or paddlers take their places and cast off. In canoes, all passengers should be seated in the bottom with the weight well balanced over the keel.

Trimming a Boat or Canoe.—Trimming a small craft is simply a matter of adjusting the weight of occupants and duffel so that the boat or canoe is in balance, not only from side to side but fore and aft as well. All weight should tend to center amidships, the place in the craft of greatest carrying capacity. When the weight is disposed too far forward, it is said of the craft that it is "down by the head" and it will be difficult to maneuver. Likewise, if the weight is more aft, the boat or canoe will be "down by the stern" and not row or paddle easily. If the weight is not evenly distributed from side to side, the craft will list (lean) toward the heavy side.

Rowing and Paddling in Heavy Weather.—There is little excuse for being caught by a storm far from shore in a small boat or canoe. In the first place one should never be very far away from the safety of the land and secondly, the good boatman or canoeist should be skilled in reading the signs which indicate changes in the weather and be prepared to run for shelter. Here, however, the human factor proves once again to be fallible because users of boats and canoes, many times expert, do frequently get caught in a sudden blow. The wind itself, unless it is extremely violent, will rarely cause a rowboat or canoe to capsize unless the weight of the occupants is very high but the waves which get up in a few minutes are likely to fill or overturn the craft if some means of prevention are not taken.

A single oarsman in a rowboat may, if his boat is not too low in the stern, turn and run before the wind if that will take him to shore and safety. If his boat is down by the stern, especially if he is carrying a passenger in the stern sheets, he should turn the bow of his craft into the wind and merely use the oars to keep pointed upwind as he drifts down before it. Following seas come aboard over the stern and swamp a boat too frequently to permit running before the wind unless the boat is riding high and lightly.

Canoes are double-ended craft being of the same shape and height fore and aft. A single paddler shifts his position to meet a blow to a point almost directly amidships. If he chooses to run before the wind he will kneel just a few inches back of amidships; if he paddles into the wind, his weight will be slightly forward. In this position, the wind itself will aid in keeping the canoe pointed. A sudden storm may get up such a high wind velocity that the paddler is powerless to direct his canoe. In this case, if he will stretch out flat in the bottom of his craft, he will find that it will neither fill nor capsize but be borne along before the wind like a fallen leaf. Unless one is very close to a dangerous lee shore and is being driven onto it, there will be little danger in drifting before the wind in this manner. Summer storms of this character usually blow themselves out in a few minutes and when their force is spent, the paddler can make his way back to safety. Two paddlers under such circumstances behave in much the same fashion. They may move to a point amidships as close together as they can conveniently swing their paddles and either head into the wind or run before it, or they may lie in the bottom.

Loss of Oar or Paddle.—The loss or breakage of an oar or paddle is serious only to novices who have not the experience or knowledge to offset the handicap. If every rowboat and canoe were equipped with extra oars or paddles, the loss of one would mean nothing more than temporary inconvenience. If, however, a person finds himself in the situation of having but one oar, he may readily unship it from its lock and use it as a paddle, handling the boat as he would a canoe. His progress will be slow because of the greater weight of the craft but eventually he will reach shore somewhere. This is, however, a very crude and inefficient way of meeting the situation. In many parts of the world even quite large boats are propelled customarily by sculling with a single oar over the stern, instead of rowing. The art of sculling should be learned early in the experience of the boat user so that in case he cannot row, his one remaining oar may be used not only to propel the boat but to steer it as well, with some efficiency.

Loss or breakage of the paddle from a canoe involves no grave danger to the trained canoeist in calm or moderate weather. Satisfactory progress may be made towards shore by kneeling amidships and, while holding the gunwale on one side, tilting the canoe slightly to the opposite side and taking several paddling strokes with the free hand. Then, just before the canoe begins to swing too sharply off course, the position and weight is shifted to take several strokes on the other side. By working

Fig. 28. Hand-paddling to recover lost paddle.

alternately in this manner and adjusting one's position slightly forward or aft satisfactory progress may be made and steering control obtained.

Sculling can be used successfully to drive a boat into the wind or across a moderate current but paddling a boat with an oar or hand-paddling a canoe is not particularly effective under similar conditions. All that can be done in such a case is to go with the wind or current and strive to cut a long diagonal course to shore.

Falling out of a Boat or Canoe.—Falling out of a boat or canoe is a very embarrassing experience since there is rarely any good reason why a person should fall overboard. Usually, it is the result of some unthinking act such as reaching too far out, standing and losing the balance, or it occurs while trying some stunt which involves balance. That it can be serious for those who swim quite well is a fact not generally understood by most people.

Commonly, the boat or canoe does not fill or capsize at all unless the desperate grasp of the occupant overturns it as he falls out. Usually, the craft slides out from under the victim as he falls and, righting itself, drifts away.

No time should be lost by the victim in returning to surface and making for his craft, for if it once gets under way before even a mild breeze it will drift more rapidly than the victim can swim and he will only exhaust himself in trying to catch it. If the boat or canoe cannot be caught (and a few strokes in its direction will tell) the victim should take stock of his position and determine how best to get out of the situation. Hampering outer clothing, if the person is clad, should be removed before striking out for the nearest point of safety. If the swim is to be a long one, a long slow swimming stroke should be employed with frequent rests in a floating position to conserve energy. Little energy should be wasted in attempting to signal for aid. If no one saw the accident occur or notes the empty craft floating about, it is not likely that waving the arms will attract attention. Thus, alternately swimming and resting, the victim can make shore if fortune is with him.

If the victim falls from a boat but does not lose contact with it he should rest for a little while hanging lightly to the gunwale. When he has gathered his wits and a measure of strength, he should swing around to the stern. Placing both hands on the upper edge of the transom and starting from a straight arm hang he should lunge, press and kick his way upward to breast over the edge in much the same fashion as he would "breast out" of a pool or onto a float. If the head, shoulders and chest are brought into the boat by this means, he can then press up and forward and contrive to draw the rest of the body inboard. If effort is made not only to bring the upper body above the stern of the boat but also to bring the boat under the body, the first try will usually be successful.

To get into a canoe is not quite so simple but it can be done with little difficulty. The victim holds to the near gunwale with both hands while he kicks vigorously to bring his body up to a horizontal plane at the surface of the water. He should then

Fig. 29. Getting into a canoe from deepwater. 1. Coming in over gunwale.

Fig. 30. Getting into canoe from deep water. 2. Weight balanced over gunwale.

be at right angles to the canoe and at a point abaft the center, where the canoe is a comfortable arm's length in width. With the arm nearer the center of the canoe, he reaches across and seizes the gunwale on the far side, with the elbow up. The other hand meanwhile continues to grip the near gunwale securely.

Fig. 31. Getting into canoe from deep water. Legs brought in last.

Aided by a vigorous leg kick and a spring, he presses and pulls on the far gunwale without allowing the elbow to drop and pushes horizontally on the near gunwale until the whole upper body is inboard. He then pivots to a sitting position in the bottom of the canoe and swings the legs in after him. Great care should be exercised to press the near gunwale only enough to get the body in over it.

Practice in getting into a boat or a canoe unaided from a position in deep water should be a part of the training of every person who uses either, in preparation for meeting such an emergency.

Capsize.—When a rowboat or canoe careens and fills with water or when it capsizes the situation is not as serious as it appears. If it is remembered that rowboats and canoes are constructed mainly of wood and carry no ballast, the fact that unless old and waterlogged, they cannot sink is quite apparent. Even steel boats have watertight compartments to aid in keeping them afloat. If the boat floats either upright or overturned the buoyancy of its materials and construction provides a ready means for preserving the lives of the occupants. In case the craft is capsized the occupants should not leave it and attempt to swim ashore unless it is being borne by wind or current into a dangerous situation.

The overturned or filled small craft offers two means of self-rescue. If righted, even though full of water, it is capable of supporting the weight of its crew, if it has not been overloaded. The victims of the accident literally swim over the gunwale of the boat or canoe and settle to a sitting position with legs widespread, in the bottom. If no pressure is applied to the gunwales and balancing is done with arms extended just beneath the surface it will be found that the filled craft has enough buoyancy to bear the all but submerged weight of the occupants. With their

Fig. 32. Best method of using swamped canoe.

Fig. 33. One method of using overturned canoe for support.

heads comfortably above the surface slow but steady progress can be made by hand-paddling toward shore and safety.

The overturned craft can also be made to sustain the weight of the victims without righting it. Because it usually catches and holds some air beneath it, the capsized canoe has greater buoyancy but in the inverted position it offers a less stable support and is more difficult to propel toward shore. A lone victim of a capsize can come back to the overturned boat or canoe and, if it is flat-bottomed, slide a portion of his weight onto the bottom over the stern. Then by balancing carefully, he can use his legs which are still in the water to kick his way toward safety. Two or more persons can hardly haul themselves upon the bottom of an overturned boat or canoe and maintain the balance. They can, however, range themselves on opposite sides of the craft and hold to each other's wrists across the keel. Wrists are held rather than hands clasped because, if the drift toward shore or the arrival of rescuers is to take some time, the hands will tire and the grasp will be loosened long before a position of safety is reached. If, however, one grasps the wrists of the other and holds until he tires, each may spell the other and rest the hands at frequent intervals. If no help appears and it is apparent that it will be necessary to drift for hours, long before complete exhaustion comes, a belt, necktie, shirtsleeve, handkerchief or rope end should be used to bind the wrists together over the bottom of the craft. The victim may then survive for some time after the strength is exhausted and even lapse into unconsciousness and still not drown if the head rests on the outstretched arms over the bottom of the canoe and keeps the face above the surface.

Almost any capsized small craft can be righted and boarded while swamped and since in practically every case it can then be hand-paddled steadily toward shore, unaffected by the wind and but little disturbed by even large waves, this procedure is

Fig. 34. Swamped rowboat used for self-rescue.

preferable to clinging almost helplessly to the upturned bottom. However, such handling for efficient self-rescue requires training and practice and very early in his canoeing or boating experience the learner should practice under completely safe conditions the procedure necessary for use in an actual emergency.

"Shaking Out" Small Craft.—"Shaking out" the water from a capsized canoe after it has been righted is a very clever means of emptying it even though some distance offshore. Properly done by a well-trained canoeist it is not, as generally believed, simply a stunt of little value except for exhibition pur-

Fig. 35. The "shake-out." 1. The thrust half empties canoe.

Fig. 36. The "shake-out." 2. The remainder is removed by
thrusts at the side.

poses. On the contrary it is a practical everyday routine accomplishment of the trained canoeist; entirely practical for one man with a canoe up to eighteen feet in length or for the concerted action of a crew even in rough water of any depth. It is not a necessary procedure in narrow streams or in cruising along shore and is not possible of accomplishment, of course, in white water. On large bodies of open water and especially in canoe sailing it is a vital and valuable safety accomplishment. It has been used successfully by crews of twelve girl campers manning a thirty-five foot war-canoe. The canoe-sailor who has mastered the technique of the "shake-out" naturally sees to it that his sailing rig is so arranged that it can be quickly cast off when the canoe is swamped and allowed to float while the canoe is being "shaken out." The canoe cruiser likewise takes care that his duffel is packed so that it will float and that only a minimum of sinkable articles are lashed within the canoe. Given the ability to shake a canoe out capably, it is surprising what can be accomplished along similar lines with other small craft such as flat or round-bottomed rowboats, skiffs and small dories.

It is possible for a well-trained man working alone in deep water to empty a sixteen foot or seventeen foot swamped canoe in less than one minute using the "shake-out." The technique is very exact and is, therefore, not so readily adaptable for self-teaching, but under the guidance of a capable instructor the fundamentals may be learned in one-half hour. When properly done rhythm and coordination play a much greater part in the "shake-out" than sheer strength.

It has been stated for years as axiomatic by organizations interested in water safety that in case of capsize one should always stick to his craft. There are, however, some circumstances under which this rule does not always apply. When a boatman or canoeist has handicapped himself by rashly taking out non-swimmers who are unable to cooperate in handling the swamped craft; if it is encumbered with non-removable rigging or motor or it becomes apparent that outside aid will not be forthcoming for some time, then it may be justifiable for a good swimmer to leave the overturned craft and make for shore. After he has done everything in his power to safeguard the other victims and long before he begins to tire he may strike out. A good swimmer can cover a distance of two or three miles, alternately swimming and resting, and be reasonably sure of reaching land where he can find another craft and people to aid in rescuing his unfortunate companions. Such an attempt is governed largely by the judgment of the swimmer. It involves knowledge of his own ability to cover the required distance; what chance there is of getting aid when he reaches shore; whether the capsized craft with its burden may not drift ashore almost as soon as he can reach it by swimming. In the last analysis, the fine judgment of the individual will determine whether the attempt should or should not be made.

White Water.— Swift running streams and the white water of tumbling rapids are no place for the tyro in small craft. White water is run in some places in high-sided bateaux handled by professionals who are highly skilled in taking these large and unwieldy craft through rapids. Small rowboats are never used under such conditions but canoes in well-trained and experienced hands are frequently run through stretches of broken water, especially on long trips. Good judgment, quick thinking and deft handling of paddle and pole gained through years of experience are essential to determine how it can be done, what course to lay over the shallows and between the rocks, how to avoid the boulders and how to thread the turbulent maze of twisting and conflicting currents. No matter how skilled the paddlers there is always the chance of being capsized which adds a spice of danger to this form of canoeing. However, if overturned and thrown into white water the canoeist is at the mercy of the current and can do little to help himself.

The experience of the lumbermen of the north woods seems to have been, that, in case of overturn in rapids, those who caught and held to the rear end of the craft, most often either came through successfully to the quiet waters below or gained a handhold on the rocks from which they could be rescued. This is not hard to understand since it is apparent that the canoe or

Fig. 37. Running rapids. For best results the paddlers get closer together than usual and keep the canoe in line with and going slower than the current.

bateau when riding ahead of the victim would act as a buffer between him and the rocks upon which he might possibly be dashed.

If the victim is unable to get a handhold on his craft as he is pitched out, he must go downward with the current until he is wedged against a rock or gains the quiet water below. Apparently, the best chance of survival lies in going completely inert as one hits the water and riding through utterly relaxed, feet foremost if possible. In certain mountainous sections of Japan long loosely-joined rafts of bamboos are habitually run down turbulent mountain streams. Like snakes they undulate along their crooked course and rarely are caught and jammed, where rigidly constructed boats of equal length would be banged and smashed to pieces. The analogy is reasonable. The relaxed body can follow the tortuous windings of the current where, if held rigid, it might be forced out of the current and crashed against an obstruction.

Swift Running Currents.—The use of boats and canoes is not limited to the quiet waters of lakes and ponds. They are used also on the rivers of the country. Ordinarily on streams, they will be found only where the water is relatively placid and the flow of the current is gentle. However, any river will have at some point in its course or at certain times, conditions in which the current will run very forcefully. A narrowing of the bed of the stream, or a steeper gradient will cause the water to accelerate its flow. The effect of the tide at the mouths of streams emptying into the sea may cause very strong currents both on ebb and flow. Heavy rains and the subsequent run-off of storm water frequently turn placid streams into raging torrents in a few hours. Anyone may have the experience of being caught in strong currents in a boat or canoe under these circumstances, but unless he is being drawn swiftly toward falls or rapids, the danger is not great. A long diagonal course toward the shore, traveling with the current, will eventually enable the person so caught to reach safety. In very fast running water much of the effort will have to be expended in keeping the craft from spinning as it is carried downward.

Safety in the Outboard Motorboat.—Little more care has to be exercised in operating the small outboard motorboat of small power and low speed than is needed in the use of ordinary rowboats. But the operation of the exceedingly small, very high-powered craft used in outboard motorboat racing presents at least one safety problem that is not found in any other type of boating. The extreme light weight of the craft and the speed at which it is operated makes it hard to control in rough water especially in turning. At high speed this type of boat frequently capsizes throwing the driver into the water. At velocities greater than forty miles an hour (and some of these boats can do almost sixty) the impact on the surface of the water for the person thrown out is much like that of hitting a pavement. Occasionally the driver strikes the water with such force as to render him unconscious. In this condition, drowning will be but a matter of a minute or two if nothing intervenes to prevent it. All drivers of high-powered boats should wear kapok-filled life jackets when operating their craft at great speed. The jacket should be equipped with a high collar which comes well up beneath the chin and the base of the skull. Then, if thrown into the water and knocked out by the force of the blow, the victim of the accident will not only float on the surface but will also have his head supported in such manner as to prevent the face slumping forward beneath the surface.

Small craft operation is a thrilling and enjoyable sport from the lazy happiness of pulling about in a clumsy old punt or flat-bottomed skiff to the thrill of sailing a sporty little dinghy in a good breeze or that of guiding a chip of an outboard motorboat at fifty miles an hour. It requires only a little swimming ability and knowledge of handling to be safe in operating most classifications of small craft and the possibilities of enjoyment in them are almost limitless. As swimming and handling ability develop, other craft, in the operation of which there is an added spice of danger and a great requirement of skill, the light canoe, the kayak, et cetera, will afford new thrills to the user and there will be little danger as he steps along from class to class and activity to activity provided he does so in a progressive and orderly manner. The danger, if any exists, will lie in attempting advanced skills before fundamental ones are mastered.

CHAPTER IV

DROWNING AND ELEMENTARY FORMS OF RESCUE

Even if all the bathers were well-qualified swimmers with a full knowledge of safety practices or, if those who are indifferent or non-swimmers would confine their activities to safe and well-supervised waterfronts, there would still be a considerable incidence of unavoidable accidents. This alone would make a knowledge of life saving almost a necessary requirement for those who frequent bathing places. A considerable number of those who seek recreation in and on the water are unable to swim, and do not distinguish between safe and unsafe practices because of lack of knowledge and skill. The frequency with which many such persons get into difficulty makes some elementary knowledge of life saving almost a necessity to anyone regardless of his swimming ability or lack of it. The development of a person's swimming skill should be paralleled by the acquirement of life saving skills commensurate with individual ability. It is not necessary to wait until one is able to swim well, before he undertakes to learn life saving. There are many ways of assisting or rescuing a drowning person which require no swimming ability at all and still others in which a little swimming skill or the ability to handle a boat is all that is needed. It is instinctive for many persons to attempt to aid anyone in grave danger but the promptings of this instinct are not always followed by a reasonable and sure course of action. The will to aid too often ends tragically for both victim and presumptive

81

rescuer. Losing one's life in an attempt to save another from drowning, in many instances, does not indicate heroism nearly as much as it does bad judgment. Certainly it has never made matters any better when the hero has drowned with the victim.

There is a whole series of forms of rescue by which drowning persons may be aided with little risk to the rescuer. These are reasonably safe methods which can and should be used under the circumstances indicated by anyone whatever the degree of his swimming ability. The swimming rescue should never be attempted if a safer means can be found to aid the drowning person.

Drowning.—The act of drowning is in itself unfortunately quite a simple process. First there is the circumstance which causes the drowning. Among non-swimmers it is most often venturing beyond the bather's depth or stepping off into a "hole" which causes the accident. Less frequently it may be exhaustion, fainting, heart failure or inability to regain the footing after being swept off balance by current or wave. This last circumstance happens not infrequently among surf bathers. In the novice class, overestimation of ability is the most common cause of drowning. Failure to make an objective in deep water due to exhaustion or cramp and resultant panic leads to many drownings. The incidence of drowning accidents among good swimmers, however, is not great. When a good swimmer drowns it may be due to bad judgment, exhaustion, cramp, illness or a blow which may temporarily render him unable to control his movements. Diving in shallow water and striking the head on the bottom and diving from a height and landing flat on the back or the front are likewise contributory causes. Among users of small craft there is quite a large loss of life, mostly among non-swimmers and largely from canoes. Something has been said hitherto about this type of accident and its prevention. These and a few other miscellaneous circumstances are the immediate causes of drowning accidents. Most of them are avoidable but a few are not because they are impossible to foresee.

Drowning may be either active or passive. The person who is seized with a heart attack, rendered unconscious by fainting or by a blow, seized by a violent cramp of the stomach, or paralyzed by fear will simply slip beneath the surface without warning. The exhausted or panicky bather will usually continue to stay on the surface for a few moments and by his convulsive agitation, advertise the fact that he is drowning. In the latter case, his movements will be either violently or feebly unrelated to each other depending on the amount of energy he possesses, causing him to bob up and down until finally with stomach filled with water and tidal air lost, he settles beneath the surface and starts his descent to the bottom. There is little evidence to support the popular belief that "a drowning person comes up twice before going down for the third and last time." If he loses his tidal air on the first downward trip and can make no move to rise again he will not of his own volition reappear at the surface. On the other hand, if he manages to hold some tidal air on each downward trip and can still make frantic clawing efforts to return to the surface the chances are he will reappear not once or thrice but, perhaps, a half dozen times. In certain rare cases a person may drown while floating about on the surface. One example of such a drowning was that of an elderly woman who, in addition to being quite stout had also fixed forward sloping neck and shoulders. As reported, she walked into the water until she was waist-deep. Then, apparently because of her extreme buoyancy, she fell forward and her legs lifted to the surface. In the prone position she was quite unable to regain her footing and, because of the peculiar malformation of the spine, could not get her face above the surface. She was picked up quite dead after drifting some fifty yards in that position.

What happens beneath the surface in the final downward plunge is well known from the descriptions of their drowning experiences given by persons who have been revived afterward and from observation in certain cases. Contrary to popular belief it is not always an agonizing experience. In some cases it has been reported that there was little discomfort in the latter stages of the drowning and others have reported a distinct feeling of chagrin at being in such a situation. In many cases it has been stated that only confusion and bewilderment preceded the lapse into unconsciousness. This is quite a different picture from that of the "whole life passing in review" conception generally held.

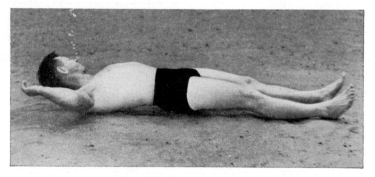

Fig. 38. On the bottom.

Whatever the case, when enough tidal air escapes from the lungs (assuming that effective motion has ceased) to cause the specific gravity of the body to be greater than that of the water it displaces, the person starts downward. The rate at which the body descends is in exact proportion to its specific gravity, but may be affected and deviated from the perpendicular by currents. As the body descends the increasing pressure of the water on the chest walls forces out the remainder of the tidal air in a thin stream of bubbles. On occasion, the glottis may be in spasm until the body reaches bottom and when it is finally released the remaining air may be lost in one great bubbling exhalation. Incidentally, both of these occurrences are telltale indicators to rescuers of the location of the body on the bottom but it must be remembered that in flowing water the bubbles will rise diagonally. There is no supporting evidence for a common belief that in water of great depth a drowned person sinks only part way and remains suspended there. It makes small difference whether the water is fifteen or a thousand feet deep, the body must inevitably settle to the bottom, if its specific gravity is greater than that of the water it displaces.

Fig. 39. Position of victim of stomach cramp.

On the bottom the body rests in a reclining position either prone or on the back. In victims of stomach cramp, the knees may be drawn up to the chin with the body lying on the side. Occasionally, in the early stages of a drowning accident, a rescuer may find the victim standing erect on the bottom but this state of equilibrium cannot continue very long. Once the body reaches the bottom it will stay there or in close proximity to it

for a period of several hours at least, but, since its specific gravity will be but little greater than that of the water itself, it will
be subject to any movement of the water. In flowing water it
will be carried by the current, tumbling and rolling along the
bottom, until it comes to rest against an obstruction or in a
back water. In swift water a strong current boiling upward may
bring it to the surface, but only for a moment before it sinks
again. When a body finally comes to rest it will not reappear at
the surface again unless and until the gases formed within it by
decomposition give it buoyancy enough to offset the pull of
gravity.

Evidence gathered over a period of many years shows
quite positively that a vast majority of drowning accidents occur very close to shore. It can be reasonably stated that if the
shore lines of all inland and coastal waters were to be paralleled
diagrammatically by an imaginary line forty yards out, it would
be found that in the area thus encompassed a vast proportion
of the drowning accidents among bathers occur. Accidents to
users of small craft usually occur outside of that area. No formula is necessary to prove that any able-bodied person may be
required at any time to rescue someone in distress in the water. The problem lies with every individual to act swiftly and intelligently within the limits of his capacity to aid.

The Value of Life Saving Knowledge and Training.—
If everyone had the ability to meet an emergency with rapid and
clear application of thought and follow it immediately with
quick action, little instruction in the technique of life saving
would be necessary. The person who has this capacity, however, is a rarity in mankind. All the rest react with varying degrees of slowness mentally, and may or may not be able to respond physically, in the face of an emergency. For proof of this
anyone needs only to recall in his own experience his reactions
in a crisis which involved grave danger to someone: the kaleido-

scopic whirl of mental images distorted by emotion; the confusion of nerve impulses ungoverned in their release and the resultant random and aimless movement; the uncontrolled re-
flexes occasioning spasmodic action of muscles; and even the
dumb immobility brought about by fear. Any or all of these
have been the common experience of men in such a situation.
Fortunately, through knowledge of what happens in drowning
accidents and practice in methods of rescue, all but a very few
persons can train themselves to react correctly in emergencies.
It can be observed readily enough that drowning accidents can
be easily classified in a few categories. Knowledge of what happens and of procedures in effecting a rescue eliminates the element of surprise and permits sure controlled action which is
semi-automatic. In short-circuiting the stimulus through the re-
flexes, reaction time is greatly speeded up.

When a drowning accident occurs any person in the vicinity, as a potential rescuer, needs to ask himself only two ques-
tions. "Have I the ability to aid?" "By what means can I help?"

Rescues may be divided roughly into four classes. First,
those that may be made from shore; second, rescues made by
wading; third, by swimming; fourth, from small craft and with
special equipment.

Assists or Elementary Rescues Made from Shore

Quite commonly, assists are made from shore and so easily
and quickly are they accomplished that little attention is given
to them, it being assumed that anyone can help in this way
without particular instruction. However, it happens occasionally that the victim pulls the rescuer into the water with him and if
that person is a non-swimmer or is clutched by the victim the
peril becomes twofold.

Reaching Assists.—Accidents which happen within
arm's length of the shore occur most frequently in swimming

pools with perpendicular sides, off the edges of floats and rafts, in streams below overhanging banks. In all such cases the procedure for giving aid is the same; that is, for the rescuer to drop to a prone position with the upper body extended over the water without overbalancing, and extend a hand to the victim. If

Fig. 40. The hand reach.

Fig. 41. The leg extension.

the victim is beyond hand reach the position may be reversed. Thus with a good handhold or grip on the edge and the body in the water the fully extended legs may be presented to the victim to grasp.

On shelving and somewhat precipitous shores or on trees overhanging the surface one of two things is necessary for the self-preservation of the rescuer; either he must have his feet securely braced and center of gravity somewhat back of the vertical or, he must have a good handhold on a firm branch, bush or rock before he attempts to grasp the victim. In seizing a victim who is being carried along by a swift current, the rescuer must brace and merely strive to hold until the body comes to a horizontal position. Once on the surface where the grip of the current is not so strong, the victim can be drawn to shore. If two people are present, one should always act as anchor for the other, holding him by the feet or one hand.

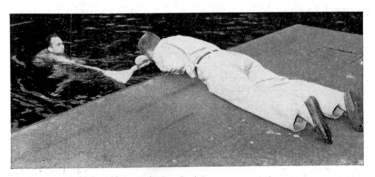

Fig. 42. Extension using towel.

Extensions for Reaching Assists.—When the victim is just out of reach a quick survey of the immediate vicinity will almost always reveal something that will serve as an extension of the reach of the arm. This may be the coat the rescuer is wearing, which if whipped off quickly and held by one sleeve may be flung outward another arm span. The branch of a tree, a fishing

Fig. 43. Extension using pole.

rod, an oar, a paddle, a pole, or a boathook seized and shoved endmost to the victim will give him the handhold he needs so that he may be pulled in. An instrument of this kind pressed firmly against the chest even when the victim is beneath the surface will almost invariably be seized instinctively provided the victim is still conscious.

Use of the Hand Line.—Occasionally on waterfronts, especially at wharves and docks, lengths of line are to be found. Properly handled they can be used effectively for aiding victims who may be beyond the reach of a boathook. By simply coiling the line and throwing one-third of the coil while allowing the other two-thirds to feed off the other hand, it can be extended for thirty or forty feet. When the victim has a firm handhold, he can be hauled in hand-over-hand, care being taken to pull fast enough to keep the head on the surface but not so fast as to tear the line from his hands. To a low shore or float the victim can be hauled directly, but at a wharf, a bridge or a vertical embankment the procedure is as follows: The victim is hauled in until he is in contact with a piling, an abutment or a wall. Here he is instructed to take two or better, three round turns of the line about his body and to hold both the end and the standing part of the line secure. When this is done he can be hauled upward to safety. The average person cannot retain an ordinary handhold for more than a few feet above the surface. If the victim is so far gone that he cannot obey instructions it will be necessary for someone to descend and secure him before he can be hauled to safety.

Fig. 44. Correct position for throwing line.

The Ring Buoy.—The first piece of apparatus devised solely for aiding a person in danger of drowning was the ring buoy. This was devised by an Englishman by the name of Carte in the 1940's and has been used extensively ever since, the world over. The ring buoy is a ring shaped object made of cork, covered with canvas having a looped life line affixed to its outer circumference. As it is used on ships it is a large, rather heavy affair which can be lifted from its rack and dropped overside when anyone goes overboard. Soon after its invention it was brought ashore for use on piers and bridges where people were likely to get into difficulty. At best it was always a cumbersome apparatus since it could only be dropped into the water and because it was a free-floating device it could not be retrieved for a second attempt if the victim could not reach it. Later a line was attached to the buoy and then some genius whose name unfortunately is lost conceived the idea of reducing the size of the buoy to permit of its being hurled to the victim, not so much for support, as for a float for the line and something for the drowning person to seize and hold to while being drawn ashore. The ring buoy now in use, other than on ships, is distinctly a throwing apparatus and requires a special technique and skill for successful use. By this means, the rescue range from shore has been increased to a maximum of seventy-five feet although it is most effective between forty-five and sixty feet. It is to be found almost everywhere as standard life saving equipment, where there are water hazards.

The throwing ring buoy in its present form is fifteen inches in diameter and weighs about two and a quarter pounds. To it is attached by means of an eye splice fixed on the buoy itself sixty feet of $\frac{3}{16}$ inch manila line rove through a four inch wooden "lemon" at its extreme end. When properly mounted the line is coiled on four wooden spindles on a frame with the buoy itself hung on the topmost spindle. If hung correctly the

buoy and the coiled line can be seized with one movement of
the arms and brought into readiness for use.

Throwing the Ring Buoy.—The technique of throwing
the ring buoy is not difficult to master but accuracy is acquired
only by practice. The following procedure should be used. The
rescuer stands facing the water in a semi-crouched position. If
he is right-handed, the left foot is advanced in a half-stride position. The buoy is held in the right hand with a hooked grasp on
the circumference of the buoy itself. A loose bight of the line is
allowed to hang in front of the thrower and the left hand, with
the fingertips forward, holds the coil loosely somewhat in front

Fig. 45. Correct position for throwing ring buoy.

of the left thigh. The lemon attached to the end of the line is dropped to the ground and the thrower stands with his left foot on the line. This is done to make sure that the whole line is not carried into the water by the cast. To start the throw, the buoy is allowed to hang loosely in the hand at the right side, a sight is taken on the victim and the arm is swung backward to shoulder-level. Then in pendulum fashion it is swung forward with considerable vigor and as the hand reaches the level of the eyes, the fingers straighten and release the buoy. The left hand meanwhile is swung more to the front, the body is inclined outward as if to follow the flight of the buoy and if the trajectory of the throw is correct, the loops of line feed off the fingers of the left hand, following through the air and settling on the surface after the buoy has struck the water. The object of the thrower is not to hit the victim but to drop the buoy a bit beyond him and draw it into his grasp. In a crosswind, allowance should always be made for its effect upon the flight of the buoy. The throw should be made up-wind and even if it lands a little out of reach of the victim it will speedily drift down to him. If the throw is short or too far out of reach, no time should be wasted in trying to maneuver it into position. It should be retrieved immediately, by hauling in hand-over-hand and allowing the line to fall at the feet as it will. When the buoy is once more in hand, the thrower stands clear of the loose coils and with his foot still anchoring the end of the line, makes another cast.

When the victim grasps the buoy, the rescuer in his eagerness to bring him in must not pull too violently or he will jerk the buoy from his hands. A steady even pull is employed until the victim's body comes up to the horizontal position, then the speed may be increased as the line is brought in hand-over-hand. In landing a victim on a float or low dock care must be taken that he is not lost within reach. Occasionally the victim will release his hold on the buoy, reach for the landing stage and miss his grasp. As he comes near, the rescuer should drop down on his knees and seize the victim's wrist or wrists as he comes riding in, preparatory to hauling him to safety.

Only one other method of throwing the ring buoy is recommended. From bridges, some landing-stages where railing is placed about the edges, and from boats, the vertical swing of the arm cannot be used. Under such circumstances the cast is made with a side horizontal sweep of the arm at shoulder level. In all other respects the procedure is the same as that described in the previous method.

Free Floating Support.—For assisting a drowning person from shore there remains to be considered only free-floating supports. By this is meant those objects which may be dropped, thrown or pushed to a drowning person over which there can be no control by the rescuer once they are launched. Examples of these are boards and planks, oars and paddles, stranded logs, life buoys without lines and canoes and boats unequipped with

Fig. 46. Pushing plank to victim.

Fig. 47. Floating log used for support.

paddles or oars. It must be recognized that these are temporary expedients designed to give the victim relief momentarily and that they must be followed quickly by such measures as may be necessary to bring him to shore.

Wading Rescue

Victims of accidents in shallow water, when other aid is not readily available, can be helped by wading to the rescue. It is not necessary for the rescuer to have a knowledge of swimming so this may be considered as another type of assist which it is possible for anyone to make. Such accidents are of common occurrence and range in seriousness from the beginning swimmer who cannot recover to the horizontal position, to the surf bather knocked off his footing by a "smoking" breaker, or the non-swimmer in a "hole." For the average case of this kind, nothing more is needed by the persons rendering assistance than a cool head, a firm stance and a sure grip on the victim to place him on his feet or pull him to shore. It is always advisable for the rescuer to grasp the victim rather than to allow the victim to take hold. The back of a wrist, a strap of the bathing suit, the t collar, the chin or the hair offers a secure handhold for the uer.

Assisting victims in "step-offs" or on sharply shelving bottoms is much more difficult for a wader. To get within reach of the victim often necessitates wading into shoulder-deep water where, because of increased buoyancy little leverage is possible. Under these circumstances the rescuer should always keep the body inclined backward toward the shore and upon seizing the victim should attempt to draw him in very slowly. A quick jerk will almost invariably cause the rescuer to lose his balance and fall forward into deep water and into the arms of the victim with results which may end in disaster for both. Until firm footing is reached it is always advisable for the rescuer to stay between the victim and the shore. There is an alarming tendency frequently displayed to draw the victim past the rescuer and give him a boost or a shove toward shore. For a swimmer this is not necessarily a dangerous practice but in other cases it happens too often that the act of boosting the person becomes sacrificial; that is, while the victim is being pushed to safety, the recoil of the effort may cause the rescuer to fall or step back into deep water and drown if he is a non-swimmer. In only one

Fig. 48. Correct position—wading rescue.

circumstance is it advisable for the rescuer to place himself between the victim and deep water. In surf-bathing, when a bather has been knocked over by a breaker, if the rescuer is nearby, and the water shallow, he should move over as quickly as possible and place himself in line with the victim so that the runback will bring the victim to him. Bracing himself securely he should block the victim's rush seaward and while holding him securely should make no attempt to move shoreward until the runback is neutralized by the next incoming breaker. In heavy surf, this process may have to be repeated two or three times before gaining the beach.

Another type of shallow water assist occurs not infrequently in the flowing waters of streams. Caught in the current, the victim is carried helplessly downward. If there is a riffle a little way down stream, the rescuer can run along the shore and wade out to a position where he can intercept the victim. Good judgment on the part of the rescuer is vitally necessary in rendering such aid. Two or three steps will determine whether he can stand against the current or not. If a stout stick is picked up on the bank, it will prove to be very useful as an additional support. If the current is quite strong the rescuer should take a position in line with the oncoming victim and sideward to the flow. Bracing himself he should take the shock of contact on the up-stream leg and, at the same time, seize hair, collar or arm with a stout grip. After allowing the victim's body to swing, then inch by inch, he should work his way to shore. Great care should be taken to shuffle the feet along the bottom rather than to try to step, as a lifted foot is quickly swept downward by the current and the balance lost.

Extensions for Wading Rescue.—All the auxiliary extensions employed in rescues from shore can be used to aid the wading rescuer. The coat, the fishing rod, rope or life buoy may serve the wader to bridge the gap between his wading limit and the drowning victim who may be "out of reach."

CHAPTER V

SWIMMING RESCUE

Swimming rescues are, of course, completely outside the province of the non-swimmer. There are times, however, when a weak or indifferent swimmer is present when another person gets into difficulty only a short distance beyond standing depth. One cannot say that he should let the victim drown rather than attempt to swim to the rescue if no rescue apparatus is at hand. Nine times out of ten the novice will make an attempt at rescue anyway. If it is but a matter of a half dozen strokes, an untrained person may, if he wants to take the risk, swim to a position behind the victim and seize the hair. Then, turning on the side, he should stroke hard to regain the beach. If it is found that little or no progress is being made, the novice rescuer can always let go of the victim and save himself. For greater distances, the rescuer can swim a board, plank, stick or pole ahead of him, give the free end to the victim and swim back to shore pulling the victim behind him. In like manner, a ring buoy or the coat or shirt may be used. Thus he may avoid contact and yet use his small swimming ability to advantage. No one, not even a swimmer, should attempt any other form of swimming rescue unless or until he has had training in the technique employed in swimming rescue.

The reason for this is apparent. Securing a drowning victim and bringing him to shore involves contact usually with a struggling, half-crazed person, who, because he is being stran-

gled to death, heeds only the urge to seize and climb up on anything that comes within his grasp. Furthermore, the average
swimmer who has had no training in carrying another cannot
know whether the strokes he employs so well to propel himself
are adequate to make progress with the additional weight. The
swimming rescue presents a series of problems for the rescuer
which begin on the shore or dock and do not end until he is
once more on the beach with the victim. Every differing set of
circumstances must be met by semi-automatic action on the
part of the rescuer, which is the product of careful training and
practice. There is very little time in the swift action of an attempt at rescue for the rescuer to think of a way in which to
combat unexpected conditions. The constant repetitions involved in life saving practice develop sure swift action and the
confidence in one's self so necessary to meet a situation of this
kind.

Preliminary Swimming Requirement.—A swimmer
who wishes to undertake swimming rescue training must have
reasonable water ability as a preliminary requirement. He
should be able to make a shallow dive in good form, swim a
quarter of a mile without resting or keep afloat by treading water
and swimming in place for a period of ten minutes. His category
of strokes should contain as a minimum, a good side stroke, one
of the hand-over-hand strokes (crawl, trudgen or trudgen-
crawl), and a fair semblance of a breast stroke. He should be
able to swim with ease on the back using the legs alone for a
distance of twenty yards or more. He should, of course, be capable of making a surface dive and of swimming a short distance
under water. Only if he is so equipped should he undertake this
form of life saving training.

**Preliminary Knowledge of Drowning Conditions and
Exercise of Good Judgment.**—Before swimming rescue training is actually begun, the learner should know something of the

major circumstances which occur in drowning because, when a real emergency is faced, they must be considered with lightning speed to determine what the course of action will be. First, the distance from shore and the depth of the water must be estimated to determine whether this may be a reaching, wading, equipment or boat rescue, as the swimming rescue is resorted to only if no other means are available. Second, is the victim actually drowning or is he merely in distress and not in immediate danger? Third, what means are available for making the rescue? Fourth, what will the rescuer have to do in preparation for a swimming rescue, if one is necessary?

If the victim is evidently a swimmer caught in a current, or one who is merely tired or panic-stricken, a slightly longer time interval may be allowed in going to the rescue: to obtain a boat, to sprint along the shore to a point opposite him or to get rid of clothing before plunging in. If the victim is alternately sinking and reappearing on the surface, time may be taken only to remove the more cumbersome outer garments and shoes before proceeding to the rescue. If a person sinks and fails to reappear at the surface literally no time should be wasted in going to his assistance although the time required to divest one's self of outer clothing is a matter of but a few seconds.

Taking Off from Shore.—A rescuer must be prepared to take off from any type of shore, embankment or dock, so the

Fig. 49. Taking off from a dock. The long shallow dive.

problem of entering the water under varying conditions is the first one to be encountered by the prospective life saver. Where water and bottom conditions are known and there are three feet

Fig. 50. Taking off from shore. The running header off the beach.

Fig. 51. The jump from a height.

or more of water in which to dive, the long shallow header is best. This covers taking off from the side of a pool, a float, a low dock or embankment. Since it is a very speedy way of entering the water and the rescuer is almost immediately in full stroke, it is most generally used. On a sand or shingle beach, it is customary for the rescuer to run through the shallow water with high bounding strides to mid-thigh depth and then fling himself headlong into his long shallow dive, before going into stroke. Under all other shallow water conditions where the bottom is rocky, covered with mud or the water is weed-choked, a more cautious wading advance is made to waist-depth before striking out. For heights above the water greater than three feet the manner of taking off will depend upon the judgment, knowledge of water conditions and skill of the life saver. He may use a header if there is sufficient depth of water, no hidden menaces and if his ability warrants but, in case of doubt, entry should be made feet foremost. Above ten feet it is preferable for the life saver to jump rather than spring head foremost.

Approach Stroking.—It has become almost an axiom in life saving that the rescuer should keep his eyes fixed on the victim (or the spot where he was last seen) while approaching him. It is a fixed principle also, that he must get to the victim as rapidly as possible, but at the same time conserve energy enough for the return journey. The stroke employed to reach the drowning person should, therefore, be one with which rapid progress can be made without tremendous expenditure of energy and it should be swum in such a manner as to enable the gaze to be fixed constantly on the victim. Thus, if a hand-over-hand stroke or breast stroke is employed the head must be carried high and face forward at all times. The novice should practice both types of stroke with adaptations over varying distances to determine which is more useful and easier of execution.

Fig. 52. Approach stroking—head high.

Approaching a Victim

Principles of Approach.—Contact with the victim is based on still more fixed principles. The rescuer must be in position to seize the victim without being caught himself, turn him about if necessary, bring the victim's face above the surface so that he may breathe, level him off in a horizontal position and put him into a carry. The victim is generally in a vertical position, head thrown back, arms extended forward and upward, clawing madly at the water. It is necessary, therefore, for the rescuer to avoid the grasp of the victim, put him under control, boost him to a horizontal position and get under way for the carry. For the varying conditions under which these things have to be done, three types of approach have been devised.

Rear Approach.—If the victim can be approached from behind, with little loss of time the rescuer swims to a point directly behind and close to the victim's back. Quickly, the life

Fig. 53. Leveling position from rear approach—surface view.

Fig. 54. Leveling position from rear approach—underwater view.

saver reverses his position, changing from the horizontal swimming plane to one in which the legs are well forward of his chest. The legs are separated and ready to deliver a series of thrusts as soon as contact is made. The kick to be used is by preference the one the life saver uses in swimming on the back with the legs alone. This will be either an inverted scissors or a breast stroke kick, never the flutter-kick of the crawl. The regular scissors may be used if strong enough to accomplish the purpose.

Leaning backward, the rescuer then seizes the chin of the victim by shooting his hand forward quickly over the shoulder and close to the neck. The chin is cupped firmly in the palm of the hand, care being taken that no pressure is applied to the throat. Using the shoulder of the victim for leverage by resting the forearm upon it, the head is drawn up and back, as the rescuer strokes vigorously with the legs and the free arm. As the victim approaches a horizontal position and is under way, he is placed in a carry. The rescuer should shift the victim into the carry at the earliest possible moment because control is limited in the leveling process.

Under-water Approach.—Few persons drown facing away from shore. By some means they generally manage to turn toward land in their struggles to reach a place of safety. As the rescuer most frequently comes from the shore, he is faced with the problem of contacting and turning the victim about from a position directly in front of him. Two methods of approaching have been devised for use in this situation.

If the victim's head is still at the surface as the rescuer nears him, the procedure is as follows: At a point six feet or more away, the life saver does a quick surface dive, descending almost perpendicularly to a position below the level of the drowning person's feet. At that point he turns and swims upward on a diagonal toward the victim's knees. The eyes are kept open and the gaze fixed on the victim at all times in the surface dive. If the water is clear, every movement can be noted. If the water is cloudy, the outline of the victim's body may be seen against the light as the rescuer swims upward to the knees. Just before contact is made, the rescuer takes a crouching position

Fig. 55. Underwater approach—the surface dive.

Fig. 56. Underwater approach—the swim-in.

Fig. 57. Underwater approach—position for turn.

with the legs slightly forward of the chest. When the opportunity comes, the rescuer seizes the legs just above the knees and
with one hand on the front of one thigh and the other on the
back of the other thigh, the victim is turned about. The rescuer
then slides up behind the victim keeping contact with the hands
on the victim's sides at all times until he nears the surface. The
hand is then thrust over the shoulder to grasp the chin and the

same process of leveling off as employed in the rear approach is continued. There is a pronounced tendency among novices to boost the victim after the turn is made. As it only succeeds in lifting the victim's head above water for a moment and then dropping it far beneath the surface, this practice should be avoided from the very beginning of the learning process. At night or in extremely dark or muddy water, the surface dive is made in line with the victim and the victim's legs discovered by groping.

Front Surface Approach.—If the life saver nears the victim and finds that his head is beneath the surface and one or both arms are showing, he should waste no time by making a surface dive. Instead, the swimming position is reversed exactly as it was in the rear approach. At arm's length from the outstretched hands, the rescuer watches his opportunity to seize one of the wrists. Reaching in with a swift movement of the arm, the rescuer seizes the back of the wrist, either right to right or left to left. If the grasp is missed, a quick stroke of the legs will

Fig. 58. Front approach showing reversed position of rescuer.

drive the rescuer back and away from the clutch of the victim. When a firm grip is secured, the rescuer immediately leans back, pulls the victim's arm across the body, twisting the wrist in line with the pull. Simultaneously, the legs deliver a series of quick short thrusts thereby aiding in turning the drowning person about and getting under way. When the victim's back is fully turned to the rescuer, the chin is seized in the free hand, the wrist is released and the leveling process is completed in the same manner as in the rear approach.

Approach to Submerged Victim.—If the victim disappears beneath the surface during the approach from shore, the rescuer should pause just short of the spot where he went down, long enough to determine whether or not he is coming up again. With the face buried in the water, the rescuer can in a few seconds scan the bottom, provided the water is clear, and locate the victim. If it is apparent that the victim is down for good, the rescuer should immediately surface dive, cut behind him, seize the chin and the nape of the neck or the hair and draw him to the surface. Again at the surface he should level off as in the rear approach.

Learning Process for Approaches.—The learning process for the approaches is not difficult. One skill is fundamental to the first three methods and that is for the life saver to be able to reverse the position of his body quickly and easily. Practice is begun, therefore, by swimming the breast stroke, a hand-over-hand or a side stroke and at a given point reversing the position quickly and returning a short distance toward the starting point, on the back. The reverse is made most skillfully by lifting the head, pressing straight downward with the forward arm or arms, rounding the back, drawing the knees to the chest and, immediately, extending them forward and downward in a spread position ready to deliver a kick. The same technique should be used in reversing the position in the under-water approach, the reverse being made as the learner reaches the victim's feet.

All the approaches are practiced with a subject on the shore, before being tried in the water. At first, slowly and with care the positions and movements are followed through in sequence. When thoroughly mastered the action is speeded up until it becomes semi-automatic. The learner then proceeds to chest-deep water and practices the approaches and timing for the quick reverse and leveling. Later they are practiced in deep water under conditions similar to those in drowning accidents. Novices should resist the tendency to become single-handed; they should use both left and right hands throughout the practice period.

Blocking and Parrying Victim's Holds

Not infrequently a rescuer comes within range of the victim's grasping hands. This may happen through faulty judgment, an unanticipated set of a current or wash of a wave, or an unexpected movement by the victim himself. Whatever the cause may be, if the life saver sees that he is so close that he is about to be grasped he must do something quickly to avoid being caught. A method of blocking and one of parrying the grasp have been devised to meet this situation. Either one may be used effectively.

The Block.—When the rescuer finds that he is too close to the victim to make a correct approach, he simply extends his forward arm and places the hand with fingers spread against the upper part of the victim's chest. Keeping the arm rigidly extended he reverses his position. The victim will, of course, immediately seize the arm but will be quite unable to climb to the rescuer's head and shoulders. If the distance to safety is not too great, the rescuer may leave the victim in this position and swim toward the shore. If the rescuer wishes merely to break the grip and get away, both feet are brought up and placed against the victim's stomach or the lower part of his chest. A vigorous shove (not a kick), will then serve to release the grip on the arm. This is not good life saving technique, however, and

Fig. 59. The block.

Fig. 60. The block and carry.

should be used only when the rescuer is in distress through lack of air or from swallowing water. Good life saving consists not merely of releasing the victim's hold, but also of turning him about and leveling him off for a carry. To accomplish this from the blocking position just described, the free hand is brought up under the victim's elbow, seizing it in a forking grip with the thumb on the inner side of the arm. A quick shove up and across

Fig. 61. The block and turn.

the blocking arm will serve to release the victim's grasp and, at the same time, turn him about. The chin may then be secured in the hand that was used for blocking and the same leveling process employed as in the rear approach.

The Parry.—A much more skillful method of avoiding a hold which accomplishes the same purpose without allowing the victim to grasp the rescuer is the one in which a pivot is employed. In this method, the rescuer catches from beneath one of the outflung arms just above the elbow in a forked grip with the thumb on the inside. This may be left to right, or right to left. Without reversing, the life saver rolls on to the side, face toward the victim. A quick lift on the arm slides it over the head and the rescuer, pivoting to a position on the back, slips beneath the victim's armpit and emerges behind him retaining the grip upon the arm until the victim's chin is secured with the free hand.

Fig. 62. The pivot parry.

The learning method follows the usual course; that is, first on land, then chest-deep and lastly in deep water.

Release Methods

The worst possible condition that a rescuer can face in a drowning accident is to be caught and held by the victim. If every approach attempted were made correctly and conditions were always favorable the rescuer would never get into the clutch of the victim and there would be small use for release methods; but, unfortunately, judgment is oftentimes faulty and natural conditions cannot be altered to suit emergencies. Miscalculation of distances, unexpected movements of the victim, and, occasionally, the motion of the water itself oftentimes put the rescuer within reach before he is aware of it.

Reactions of the victim are of striking similarity in practically all cases. Immediately after seizing the well-intentioned life saver, his instinct seems to be to throw the head back and

Fig. 63. Victim struggling to reach surface.

climb to the highest point attainable which is, of course, the rescuer's head. If he seizes a wrist, it is certain that he will come up the arm hand-over-hand until he can reach the rescuer's head and shoulders, unless abruptly checked. Once a grip is attained about the rescuer's head, the victim strains upward madly to get away from the water and to get air. In the very act of struggling upward, his weight tends to force the rescuer's head beneath the surface. It is at this point that the inexpert rescuer does precisely the wrong thing. He resists with all his power the force that is being exerted to press him downward and throws his head back so that he may breathe. In so doing, he sustains the victim in the high position and makes an angle between the head and neck which most effectively helps the victim to maintain his hold. A little forethought will demonstrate clearly that the last place the victim wants to go is below the surface and that, if the head is inclined forward with the chin tucked well in, the victim's hold is much less secure and easier to release. If the rescuer not only allows his head to be pressed beneath the surface, but also aids and abets the act by swimming downward until the victim's head is well below the surface, he will find that in most cases the victim will let go and strive to keep his head above water. A hand placed on the front and another on the back and a quick pivot of the victim's body will serve to turn the back to the rescuer, whereupon the rear approach may be employed to put him under control.

For the rare case in which the victim does obtain and maintain a firm hold upon the rescuer's wrist or neck and head (generally the result of a convulsive tightening of the grasp at the approach of unconsciousness), release methods have been devised in which the application of powerful leverage is ingeniously employed to break the grip. These releases are few in number because they are related only to the holds that are applied to the head, neck, and arms. It is conceivable that a drowning person could get a grip upon the rescuer's legs or about his waist by some peculiar means, but so long as he remains below the surface he can cause little or no inconvenience for the rescuer since his dead weight submerged is neutralized by his buoyancy. In other words, unless he starts to climb he cannot drag the rescuer downward. If, however, the victim gets his weight over the rescuer's head and shoulders which he most surely will as he climbs upward, he can endanger the life of the rescuer by forcing his head beneath the surface if the hold is not released in some manner.

Head Release. (Front).—The most common of all the erroneously-labeled "death grips" is the hold secured from the front known as the front headlock. The victim clasps the rescuer about the head with his arms and turns the face outward and upward at the side of the rescuer's head. With the legs, the victim may "scissors" the rescuer's waist. If the distance to shallow water is but a few feet or the victim is a small child it may be quite unnecessary to release the hold. In this case the rescuer, employing the breast stroke, just swims the victim to shore. The position is entirely favorable to swim easily, to talk to the victim and to prevent water from washing over the face.

If it is advisable to release the victim's hold the following procedure is employed: As soon as the victim's arms are felt encircling the head, the rescuer's chin is tucked well into the throat, a quick "bite" of air is taken and he submerges taking the victim with him. If the victim does not let go voluntarily, the rescuer must release the hold. If the victim's head is at the right side of the life saver, the right arm is brought up and over the encircling arm and the hand placed securely against the victim's right cheek with the little finger laid against the side of the victim's nose and the thumb hooked under the jaw. The left hand is brought up beneath the victim's other arm and seizes it in a forking grip, thumb inside, just above the elbow. In one continuous movement, the victim's head is pressed out and around with the right hand while the left hand is lifting and pressing the arm over the head and sweeping it across to the far side. The hold released, the pressing movement is continued un-

Fig. 64. First method. Front head-hold release. Hands in position.

til the victim's back is to the rescuer. The left hand continues to hold the arm, until the right hand can be shifted from the victim's face, over the shoulder, and to the chin to level in the same manner as in the rear approach.

If the victim's head is at the rescuer's left side, the method is simply reversed; that is, the left hand is placed on the left cheek and the right hand takes the victim's left arm.

Scissors holds on the body are rarely held after the head hold is released but if this happens the rescuer uses one hand or fist between the ankles to unlock the crossed feet.

Fig. 65. First method. Front head-hold release. Hold released.

Fig. 66. First method. Front head-hold release. Ready to level.

Alternate Method. (For Front Head Hold Release).—
Another and superior method for releasing the front head hold
provided a body scissors has not been applied is to use a "press-
away." To do this, both arms are extended to the front and
placed against the victim's body with the heels of the hands
against the abdomen and the extended fingers and thumbs
grasping the sides. This effectively blocks any attempt on the
part of the victim to secure a "body scissors" with his legs.
Then, by lifting and pressing, the victim's body is pushed back
and up to the horizontal position. As a natural reaction to this

application of pressure, the rescuer's body will be forced back
and downward until the victim has only an insecure grip on the

Fig. 67. Alternate method. Front head-hold release. Getting
ready to press.

Fig. 68. Alternate method. Front head-hold release. The press.

Fig. 69. Alternate method. Front head-hold release. The turn.

Fig. 70. Alternate method. Front head-hold release. Getting ready to level.

back and top of the rescuer's head which a little more pressure and a hunching of the shoulders will cause to slip off. One hand is then placed on the victim's front and the other on the back and he is quickly turned to a face-up position, whereupon, with the rescuer stroking vigorously, the chin is seized and the victim brought to the surface and leveled off as in the rear approach.

Head Release. (Rear).—Occasionally, it happens that a swimmer is caught from behind by another bather or by a victim of a boat or canoe upset. Such a situation could hardly occur

Fig. 71. Rear head-hold release. Hands in position.

in actually making a rescue as it is not conceivable that the life
saver would turn his back to the victim and allow himself to be
grasped. Usually it develops as the result of panic. A non-
swimmer, sliding into deep water, an exhausted novice trying
to reach a float, a swimmer seized with cramp or a canoeist
pitched into the water, becoming panic-stricken will grasp the
unsuspecting swimmer if he happens to be within reach. There
can be no preparation for approaching or parrying as the hold
is applied without warning.

As the swimmer feels the arms encircling his head, he must
do two things automatically; tuck his chin to prevent the victim

Fig. 72. Rear head-hold release. Leverage applied.

Fig. 73. Rear head-hold release. Under control.

from seizing his throat, and get a "bite" of air. He then starts downward taking the victim with him. If the victim releases his hold, the swimmer pivots about, places one hand on the front and the other on the back and turns the victim about, whereupon he picks up the chin and levels him off in the usual manner.

If it is necessary to release the hold, the swimmer seizes the hand of the lower arm with one hand and grips the elbow of the same arm with the other. By twisting the victim's hand outward and applying pressure to the elbow simultaneously enough leverage can be applied to loosen the grip. The swimmer should then pivot inward until his back is turned to the elbow he is holding. A little added pressure on the elbow will then enable him to slip out of the hold and slide backward under the seized arm. Continued pressure is applied to carry the victim's arm to a hammer lock position in the small of the back and at the same time to turn his back to the rescuer if he has not slid to a position behind him. The hand that is on the elbow is then transferred to the chin and the victim leveled off as in the rear approach.

Wrist Grip Releases.—Not infrequently a swimmer intent upon making a rescue rides his last stroke too far thereby permitting the drowning person to catch the extended hand and wrist. Very quick action is necessary to prevent the victim from climbing up the arm and into position to get a front head hold. As soon as the wrist is seized, the rescuer reverses his position and reaches across with his free hand over the extended arms to the victim's far wrist. Taking a grip as he would hold a baseball bat or a tennis racket, with the thumb on the outer side he

Fig. 74. The double grip on one wrist. Position for breaking hold.

Fig. 75. Wrist release. Hold broken.

bears down with his forearm on the victim's extended arms, thereby submerging him. Immediately, the foot on the opposite side is swung up and over the extended arms and placed on the outer shoulder, with the heel at the base of the throat and the toes extended over the shoulder. Holding the wrist firmly, the rescuer presses the victim backward by extending the leg. As the hold is broken the legs are dropped to a scissoring position, the arm is pulled and twisted to complete the turn and to level off while the legs are stroked vigorously to stay behind the victim and get under way. The free hand is then transferred to the chin as in the rear approach.

Double-Drowning Release.—Perhaps the most common drowning accident in which it is necessary to employ a release is one in which the rescuer is not initially involved. This is the condition which is found in so-called double-drowning accident cases.

Two non-swimmers may step into a "hole" simultaneously or one may step off and carry another with him as he loses his balance. A novice, seeking to aid a victim, may be caught by

Fig. 76. Double-drowning release. In position.

Fig. 77. Double-drowning release. Leverage applied.

Fig. 78. Double-drowning release. Victims separated.

the drowning person. Even good swimmers who have had little or no life saving training may experience the difficulty of becoming involved with a drowning person under similar conditions. In all cases mentioned the results are much the same. There may or may not be a brief attempt to rescue the original victim but as soon as one grasps the other a fight to stay on the surface begins which ends usually with the exhaustion of both and their complete submersion and drowning. In this type of water accident the life saver is faced with the necessity of separating the two and hauling one to shore since there is no effective way known of rescuing two actively drowning persons simultaneously. If the rescuer saw the accident develop he should address his efforts to getting the one who got into difficulty first, leaving the novice or swimmer to shift for himself. The manner of separating the victims and effecting their rescue follows:

The rescuer swims to a position behind one of the victims.

Then he seizes that victim by the chin with both hands and bearing down with the forearms, submerges both. In submerging them he rides his weight high and brings one foot up over the locked arms. Placing the foot against the chest of the other victim just below the neck and with the heel inside, he pushes him down and away by straightening the leg (not by kicking). At the same time he pulls the one he has seized by the chin, up and back. Thus, he strips the one from the grasp of the other and as soon as the hold is released, drops into a back swimming position and levels off for the carry. After carrying the first victim to safety he may return to the assistance of the other, if his further services are not needed for resuscitation. If another life saver is at hand, he should go to the assistance of the second victim.

Learning Process for Releases.—The learning process for the releases is similar to that used for approaches. It begins on land with studied practice of individual movements and then combinations employed in effecting releases. When a certain degree of smoothness is attained, the action should be speeded up until it is semi-automatic. There should be an even amount of practice on both the left and the right arm and the right and left head positions. Front and back head hold releases are practiced standing. In the double grip on one wrist the victim kneels on one knee and in practicing the release for two persons locked, the victims take a position facing each other, sitting on the heels. The second step in the learning method is to practice the releases in chest-deep water. There, victims and rescuer stand while the holds are applied and the learner places the hands or feet in position. The releases are then made in a submerged position. The last step in the learning process is to practice in deep water. It must be remembered that if anything goes wrong in deep water, the rescuer cannot in his submerged position ask his practice partner to let go. It must be clearly understood, therefore, that before deep water practice is undertaken, slapping the shoulder or pinching the partner means, "Please let go."

Practice in the release of holds should be undertaken by two swimmers of about equal ability, preferably, by those who are engaged in learning life saving simultaneously. In the early

Fig. 79. Land drill on releases.

Fig. 80. Shallow-water drill on releases.

stages of practice, the holds are applied firmly but with no thought in mind of making the release impossible. When the release methods have become semi-automatic and the rescuer begins to feel confidence in them, the victim will simulate the frantic spasmodic actions of a drowning victim. This will help to increase immeasurably the confidence of the rescuer in his ability to meet actual conditions faced in a drowning accident. For further practice after the release methods are mastered, the victim may employ all the tricks of a good swimmer in full possession of his senses, to surprise and to attempt to confound the rescuer. Holds may be applied tightly, positions of the arms and head shifted unexpectedly, the head may be buried in the rescuer's shoulder, scissors holds with the legs applied and the release of one hold followed immediately by the application of another. All of these devices and many others as applied by the good swimmer make releasing conditions so much more difficult than they are in actual drowning cases that fear is eliminated perforce, and confidence gained by the learner.

Carrying a Victim

Drowning accidents, except in rare instances, occur in deep water. It usually becomes necessary, therefore, after making an approach or releasing a hold, to get the victim to shore and in the type of rescue heretofore described this must be accomplished by swimming. The problems connected with this task are at once apparent. The rescuer accepts the handicap of swimming not only for himself but for the victim and furthermore, he sacrifices the use of one or both arms, except in one instance, to the task of holding and controlling the victim. It can readily be seen that the usual strokes cannot be employed without special adaptation to offset the loss of the arm or arms used to hold the victim. It is evident also that the rescuer must rely greatly upon his legs to propel the double load. It is to the problem of selecting the strokes most useful for carries, and their adaptation, that the life saving student has first to apply himself for this phase of life saving.

Leg Strokes Used in Carrying.—Through long experience it has been proved that only two methods of using the legs are completely adequate to the task of carrying a victim. The scissors and the breast stroke kicks are the only ones that fulfill the requirement for power, reasonable comfort and sustained effort and even the breast stroke kick is limited to certain carries. The scissors stroke is, therefore, of singular importance in making swimming rescues. There are really only two ways of employing the scissors stroke in life saving, and each has a definite use. The regular or standard scissors with the top leg forward and the under leg back is used for all carries in which the rescuer swims on one side and the same scissoring movement

Fig. 81. The inverted scissors kick.

inverted is used when swimming on the back or the other side, thus directing the top leg backward and the under leg forward. In swimming with the regular scissors, the swimmer lies squarely on the side; in using the inverted scissors there is a tendency to roll slightly onto the back. Some swimmers learn to swim the side stroke with the scissors inverted and learn to swim on the other side by simply turning over and employing a regular scissors. The inverted scissors or the inverted breast stroke kick is used for swimming on the back.

Arm Stroke Used in Carrying.—If the type of carry used permits swimming with one arm, it is always the under arm that is free. This arm, in the side stroke, normally pulls vertically beneath the body which tends to lift the head and shoulders well above the surface. In side stroke swimming the other arm picks up the stroke and sustains the position but in swimming with a victim, if the same stroke of the forward arm is used, inevitably both rescuer and victim will be dropped below the surface in the recovery of the arm because of the loss of the compensating

Fig. 82. Shallow arm pull and regular scissors kick.

stroke. Therefore, the direction of the pull of the under arm must be changed from the vertical to the side horizontal. The shallow arm-pull, as it is called, is swept from the extended position around in front of the face some six or eight inches below the surface to a bent position in front of the chest, exactly as though the swimmer were gathering an armful of water. To recover, the shoulder is rolled back, the hand rotated until the fingertips are pointed forward palm down and the arm extended to the starting position.

The Learning Process for Strokes Used in Carrying.— The learning method consists largely of practice in three positions: swimming on one side with the regular scissors and the shallow arm-pull, swimming on the other side with the scissors inverted and shallow arm-pull and swimming on the back with the inverted scissors or breast stroke kick. (The breast stroke kick may be used in swimming on the back if it is strong and well-coordinated.)

Principles of Effective Carrying.—Out of the many methods which have been devised for carrying a victim, only four have withstood successfully the test of time and extensive application. If the factors governing effective use are considered it can readily be understood why. An effective carry must permit the victim's face to be carried above the surface at all times; it must keep the victim at or near the horizontal position constantly; it must enable the rescuer to control the victim; it must allow the rescuer the greatest freedom of swimming movement possible, consistent with his position of close bodily contact and it must, above all, permit the rescuer to assume a safe position in relation to the victim. With these principles firmly established the four methods are now presented.

Tired Swimmer Carry.—As the name indicates this type of carry is used in assisting a swimmer who has become tired but is not in immediate danger of drowning. This condition often arises when two persons are swimming side by side for some distance. One may find that he has overestimated his endurance and cannot attain his objective. The other must go to his assistance, at once, and in the easiest manner possible to conserve energy, swim the tired swimmer to shore.

To do this most easily, the swimmer moves over to the victim and instructs him to turn to a face-up floating position. He then swims to a position facing the tired swimmer and tells him to place his hands on his shoulders keeping the elbows straight, to separate the feet and to look him in the face. Thereupon, the rescuer swims a slow and easy breast stroke, pushing the victim ahead of him, meanwhile encouraging him by talking calmly about anything other than the danger involved. The recovery of the arms in the breast stroke must, of course, be along the sides of the victim. Should the tired swimmer become panicky and seize the rescuer in a front head hold and body scissors, if the distance to shore is not too great, the swimmer should make no effort to release himself but simply lower the chin to prevent a strangling grip and keep on swimming. As the victim is beneath the rescuer and has no downward pull because of his buoyancy, he can be used as a raft to paddle on, for the few re-

maining strokes necessary to gain the safety of shallow water
or the shore. If the distance to shore is great and the victim tries
to climb onto the head and shoulders of the rescuer, he should

Fig. 83. Tired swimmer carry.

Fig. 84. Tired swimmer carry. Underwater view.

submerge, use a front head hold release and after leveling off proceed with a carry taken from behind.

Hair Carry.—The hair carry, next to the tired swimmer carry, is the easiest one to learn and put into practice. The rescuer has only one point of contact with the victim, the hand in the hair; the rigidly extended arm holds the victim at a distance

Fig. 85. Hair carry.

Fig. 86. Hair carry. Underwater view.

and there is no interference with the rescuer's strokes. Since it is so comfortable and so easy of accomplishment, it is used most frequently for carrying over the longer distances. It is not particularly comfortable or reassuring to the victim, however, to be carried by the hair at arm's length from the rescuer, so it is used preferably for semi-conscious or unconscious persons.

To do the hair carry, the rescuer slides his fingers from the crown of the victim's head toward the forehead and seizes a handful of hair. Depressing the wrist and holding the arm straight, he turns on his side and tows the victim using the side stroke adaptation, either with the regular or the inverted scissors and shallow arm-pull. No effort is made to lift the victim's head above the surface; if the face is out of the water, it is sufficient.

Cross Chest Carry.—Of all the carries devised for swimming rescue, the cross chest carry has been most satisfactory to life savers and victims alike. To the life saver it has been the carry in which he has had the victim most completely under control. To the victim, the position close to the rescuer and encircled by a strong arm has meant greater security. For the average carrying distance it is most frequently used; for a struggling, panic-stricken victim, it is always employed.

Fig. 87. Cross chest carry.

Fig. 88. Cross chest carry. Underwater view.

This is the way in which the cross chest carry should be done: From a position behind the victim, the rescuer reaches over the shoulder and across the chest and grasps the side just below the armpit. The rescuer tucks the victim's shoulder securely into his own armpit and clamps his arm firmly against the chest. At the same time, the rescuer turns on the side so that the hip is directly beneath the small of the victim's back. Either the regular or inverted scissors and the shallow arm-pull are then used to swim to shore. If the inverted scissors is employed the victim will be carried somewhat to the front of the hip, the rescuer will be turned slightly toward a back swimming position and the shallow arm-pull will be somewhat shorter in range than it is when the regular scissors is used.

Head Carry.—The head carry usually is little favored by swimmers when they try it for the first time. This is understandable if it is remembered that most swimmers do not swim as strongly on the back as in other positions, especially when the legs alone are used. As a rule there is little confidence displayed by the swimmer in his first attempts to propel the double load with this carry.

If the swimmer is soundly grounded in fundamental strokes, however, there should be no lack of confidence, as a well-developed inverted scissors or breast stroke kick has ample power for the purpose. It happens, inevitably, that continued practice in the head carry results in its mastery and develops in the life saver a real liking for it. In any event, it is far too important in life saving to be neglected by the swimmer and should be considered a real factor in life saving. The head carry is primarily for rescue in rough water. When the rescuer is beset by high waves in making his way to shore, he will find that by shifting to the head carry, he can watch the advancing waves, time his kick and a lift of the arms to ride both his own head and that of the victim over the crests. Neither the cross chest nor the hair carry can be employed as effectively under such conditions.

In using the head carry, from a position behind the victim,

Fig. 89. Head carry.

Fig. 90. Head carry. Underwater view.

the rescuer places a hand on each side of the head. The palms cover the victim's ears, the fingers are extended along the jaws and the thumbs are placed on the temples. The hold is firm and by depressing the wrists, the victim's head is tilted back until the chin points directly upward. The arms are held straight. The rescuer assumes a half-sitting position in the water and strokes vigorously with the legs using either an inverted scissors or breast stroke kick. The stroke is somewhat shortened and speeded up with more emphasis on the downward and backward thrust, than on the closing of the legs. Except for occasional swift glances to check position and course, the rescuer should watch the victim's face to be sure that it is kept above water.

The Learning Method for Carries.—Like every other phase of life saving, the learning method for the carries begins on land. The placement of the hands and arms and the positions of the body are made with studied care. Hands and arms are placed in such manner that the victim is able to breathe freely and yet is firmly held.

In open water, the next step is to take the victim into chest-deep water where he is boosted to a horizontal position and towed with a simple "chin-pull." In pools, the process is the same with but one variation; the victim is pulled away from the side, the rescuer getting a start meanwhile by shoving away with both feet. The "chin-pull" is merely a prolongation of the leveling-off process used at the finish of the approaches. It is in no sense a true carry, since there is little or no control exercised over the victim. It is used in the learning process simply as a means of gaining confidence and ease and as a step toward proceeding with the regular carries.

Fig. 91. Land drill on carries.

When the "chin-pull" has become easy of accomplishment, the learner begins practice with the standard carries. Starting with a "chin-pull" since it will always be the connecting operation between approaches and carries, the rescuer learns to shift from the pull to the carry in one continuous, smooth operation. To change from the pull to the cross chest carry is done in either of two ways. If the rescuer levels the victim off with one hand and wishes to carry with the same arm, he draws the victim's head close to his shoulder, shifts the free hand to the chin and quickly slides the hand that was on the chin down and across the chest, with no loss of momentum or control. Should he desire to carry the victim with the opposite arm, he retains the grip on the chin and rolls to a position on his other side, gathering the victim with the free arm into a cross chest carry position as he turns over. To shift from the "chin-pull" into the hair carry may, likewise, be done in two ways. If the rescuer desires to carry with the same hand used for the "chin-pull," the victim must be held by the chin with the free hand while the other hand is shifted from the chin to the hair. In carrying with the free hand, the rescuer simply holds the chin until the hair is grasped. Shifting from the "chin-pull" to the head carry position requires merely that the rescuer put the free hand in place on the cheek and then slide the hand from the chin to the opposite side of the head. In all transfers from the "chin-pull" to any one of the carries it is absolutely necessary for the rescuer to keep the legs moving in short sharp strokes so that momentum may not be lost.

In practice, one variation of standard technique is permitted. Practice of the hair-carry is often punishing to the partner so instead of grasping the hair, the victim is allowed to hold one or both hands palm up directly back of and close to the crown of the head. The rescuer may then interlock fingers with the victim and tow him in that manner.

Continuing the learning progression, the learner proceeds to practice the approaches, the level and the carries in combination, at first in chest-deep water or from the side of the pool and later in water of swimming depth. In the early stages of practice, the leveling operation will be rather long but, gradually, the interval between the approach and the carry will be shortened until it is just long enough to bring the victim to the horizontal and get under way. It is dangerous to continue the "chin-pull" for any considerable distance since the victim is not fully under control.

When the approaches and carries can be made smoothly and the victim can be carried without difficulty for a distance of fifty feet or more, practice should begin to simulate actual conditions encountered in drowning accidents. The rescuer should practice approaching, leveling and carrying a fully-clad victim. He should do the approaches and carries with the handicap of himself being clothed. He should practice changing over from one side to the other and from one carry to another. Parries and releases may be substituted for the approaches and the leveling and carrying operations continued from them. The victim may struggle violently all through the carrying operation and may even break free, roll over and apply a hold which must be released before the rescuer can continue. Those who are learning life saving in pools should, at the first opportunity, practice swimming rescues in open and rough water. Wherever possible also, experience should be gained in approaching, leveling and carrying in running water. In this way good judgment may be developed in reaching a victim and swimming him to shore under adverse conditions.

Supporting a Victim

It sometimes happens that it is not feasible or desirable for the rescuer to carry a victim after he has made an approach and leveled him off. It may have been necessary for the rescuer to

Fig. 92. Supporting a victim.

plunge from a dock or wharf into a slip for example, from which he cannot extricate himself or the victim without assistance. Possibly he has reached the victim and is supporting him while assistance is on the way. There is no particular purpose in carrying anywhere under such circumstances, if a rope is being obtained or a boat is approaching, so the problem becomes one of keeping the victim afloat and conserving energy. For this purpose the simplest way to handle the victim is to put him in a cross chest carry and maintain a horizontal position with the easiest possible stroking movements and with a minimum of headway until help arrives.

Shallow Water Carries

The problems connected with a swimming rescue do not always end when the rescuer reaches standing-depth water or the edge of a pool or float, for very frequently the victim through exhaustion is quite unable to stand or help himself in any way to gain the shore, even if he is not actually unconscious. To meet this need in the most effective and expeditious manner two types of shallow water carries and one unassisted lift from deep water have been devised.

Fireman's Carry.—When the rescuer reaches breast-deep water he stands and floats the victim in front of him. (A glance will suffice to determine whether the victim must be carried to shore.) Standing opposite the victim's waist the rescuer slides one hand under the neck and slips the other over the near leg and under the farther knee. He then submerges in a squatting position with the trunk erect and the head bowed, and simultaneously rolls the victim to a face downward position above his shoulders. As soon as the victim is in this position, the rescuer straightens the legs and emerges with the victim draped across his shoulders. (Care must be taken to have the hinge of the victim's hips squarely on the back of the neck to divide the weight equally on both sides and thus prevent slipping or overbalancing.) The hand that is between the knees now reaches across and takes the victim's forward arm by the wrist and the rescuer moves shoreward.

Fig. 93. Fireman's carry. 1. Supporting position.

Fig. 94. Fireman's carry. 2. Turning onto shoulders.

Fig. 95. Fireman's carry. 3. Coming ashore.

At a convenient point as close to the water's edge as feasible, the rescuer places the victim on the ground. In doing this, the rescuer kneels on the knee which is on the victim's headside and extends the other leg diagonally forward. The wrist which is being held is released and caught with the rescuer's other hand as it swings across and the arm which is between the knees is withdrawn to encircle both legs. In one quick movement, the rescuer swings the victim's body around in front of him and bending forward allows it to slide down his extended leg to the ground, while he continues to hold firmly the arm which lies across the back of his neck. The victim is held in this half-sitting position until the free hand can be placed behind the neck, whereupon the head is lowered gently until it rests upon the ground.

The Saddle-Back Carry.—In the saddle-back carry, the weight of victim is carried just over the back of the hips. Since the center of gravity is low, strain or loss of balance is

Fig. 96. Saddle-back carry. 1. Encircling body.

Fig. 97. Saddle-back carry. 2. Legs secured.

Fig. 98. Saddle-back carry. 3. Coming ashore.

much less likely than it is in the fireman's carry. So it is particularly good for carrying a heavy victim.

To pick up the victim in this carry the rescuer stands in waist-deep water and supports the victim's body in a horizontal position. Standing at his side, facing the head, the rescuer reaches across with his outside hand, picks up the victim's far wrist and carries the arm upward until it rests across the shoulders. The near arm, meanwhile, is slipped around the victim's body close to the shoulders, where a good hold is taken. The rescuer then turns his back to the victim, releases his hold on the wrist and reaches back to gather in both the victim's legs at the knees. This action brings the victim's body across the rescuer's back just above the hips and, if the hand under the shoulder is slipped forward until it rests under the neck, the victim's head can be held clear of the water and the rescuer may then move toward shore. On shore, the rescuer kneels on both knees, toes pointed, and sits back on the heels to lower the victim to the ground.

Learning Method for Shallow Water Carries.—The learning method for the shallow water carries consists only in mastering the technique of picking up the subject, walking to shore and placing him on the ground. In the swimming pool, it is not feasible to practice the whole process without interruption because of the difficulties and dangers attendant on getting out of the water. So, in practice, the subject is lifted and carried a short distance in shallow water only, and the methods of lowering to the ground practiced later on a mat in the gymnasium or out-of-doors.

Lifting from the Water

Occasionally the life saver is faced with the necessity of getting a victim out of the water and on to the deck of a pool or a float without assistance. The procedure is always the same if

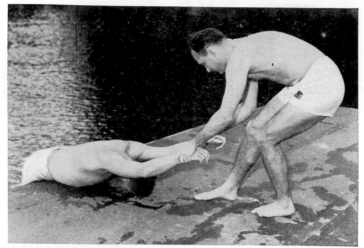

Fig. 99. Lift onto dock. 1. Upper body inboard.

Fig. 100. Lift onto dock. 2. Bringing in legs.

the victim is unable to help himself or if the water is more than chest-deep.

The rescuer brings the victim to the edge and gets a hand-hold. Always supporting the victim's head above water, he takes one hand and places it on the deck where he clamps it with his holding hand. Then he secures the other hand and places it on top of the first. With one hand holding the victim's hands fast he places the free hand over the edge and "breasts" himself out of the water. Immediately, he pivots around, secures the wrists and standing, pulls the victim's body up and over the edge. With the head and chest lying on the deck and held fast, the rescuer then uses the other hand to swing the legs inward. Great care must be exercised in lifting the victim to avoid injury to the rescuer. The lift should be made by straightening the bent legs and the lifter should avoid leaning backward as he lifts because of the danger of slipping. In lifting care should be taken also to avoid injuring the victim. The rescuer should be sure that the legs are not jackknifed under the platform or float and should not scrape the front of the victim on the edge as he is drawn out of the water.

The learning method consists of nothing more than mastery of the technique and practice in taking a subject out of the water.

CHAPTER VI

RECOVERING A SUBMERGED VICTIM

When a drowning person submerges he does not, necessarily, die immediately. Indeed, it may be some minutes before the spark of life is extinguished, even though he has ceased to breathe. Observations of eye-witnesses of drowning accidents are almost wholly unreliable because of the excitement induced by tragedy-in-the-making which prevents cool and accurate estimate of time and circumstance surrounding the accident. Yet, over a period of years, enough fairly accurate information has been gathered to demonstrate clearly that some victims have survived immersion of many minutes duration, although the vast majority, it is true, succumb within a few minutes. What the human factor is that enables one victim to survive a submersion of ten minutes or more while another under identical circumstances may live but a minute, is not known. It is not important that the potential life saver should know. All that it is necessary to consider is that a victim on the bottom must be brought to the surface and thence to the shore as rapidly as possible where first aid in the form of artificial respiration may be applied. Speed is of vital importance if rescue proceedings are begun within a few minutes after the victim disappeared. After an hour or more has elapsed the need for rapid action is not so apparent since the chance of reviving the victim is practically nil and the problem becomes one of recovering a body.

Recovery of Submerged Victim from Shore.—In recovering a submerged victim in deep water the person who lacks

154

swimming ability must confine his efforts to such means as can be used from shore. If the victim can be seen lying on the bottom, as in case of drowning off a dock or in a swimming pool, the boathook or the "shepherd's crook" offers about the only means of bringing the person to the surface, within the capacity of the non-swimmer. The boathook is a piece of boating equipment commonly found on small sail boats, motorboats and about wharves and docks. It consists simply of a blunted hook and pike affixed to a pole six or more feet in length. With it the clothing or the bathing suit may be caught and the victim drawn to the surface.

The "shepherd's crook" is a piece of rescue apparatus designed especially for use in swimming pools. With it the victim's body may be almost completely encircled and brought to the surface.

In cases where the body cannot be seen, the non-swimmer can serve best by fixing with his eye the approximate spot where the victim went down and will thus be able to point out to the swimmer who comes to the rescue, the place where the person was last seen.

Recovery of Submerged Victim by Diving.—More than ninety per cent of all submerged victims must be brought to the surface within ten minutes of their submersion if they are to have a reasonable chance to survive. Beyond that time, for the most part, the efforts of rescuers will be largely a matter of recovering bodies with little hope of revival. This fact definitely establishes the value of swimming and diving ability under ordinary circumstances since it is the quickest and most certain manner of getting the victim to the surface.

If the victim goes down even as the rescuer is swimming toward him, no time should be lost. With eyes fixed on the spot where the drowning person was last seen, the rescuer continues to swim and upon reaching that place does a surface dive. Once beneath the surface, the victim is located and the rescuer cuts in behind him. The chin, and the hair or nape of the neck are grasped, the rescuer turns and by vigorous leg stroking makes his way to the surface. Back on the surface the victim is shifted into a carry and the rescuer heads for shore.

If the victim disappears beneath the surface before the rescuer arrives or if there is some doubt about the exact spot at which he went down, the trained life saver will stop for a moment to survey the situation. First, he must determine the general area in which the victim is supposed to have sunk. Depending upon the distance from shore and the depth of the water, if known, he must plan his course of action. If other persons are present he should direct them in ways in which they may assist him. This is not time wasted for meanwhile if dressed, he may be removing his outer clothing and shoes. Of those gathered at the scene of the accident he may dispatch one to secure and man a rowboat; another may be sent to summon a doctor; a third to get blankets and first aid equipment and a fourth to locate grappling irons if any are known to be available in the immediate vicinity.

If he has to swim to the area in which he plans to dive, he must take off and move out with an easy stroke, conserving his strength and "wind" for the taxing effort of diving and swimming under water. As he moves into the area in which the victim is supposed to have gone down, he begins to look for telltale bubbles rising to the surface. If there are none and the water is reasonably clear he should swim slowly across the area with the face buried in the water and scan the bottom. Against a dark bottom, the gleam of the arms and legs of the victim can often be detected even at considerable depth. On white sand, the dark color of the hair or the bathing suit indicates the position of the drowned person. When the victim is located in this manner the rescuer does a surface dive, swims down to a posi-

Fig. 101. Locating victim on bottom.

Fig. 102. Surface dive.

Fig. 103. Underwater view of surface dive.

Fig. 104. Victim located by swimming along bottom.

tion behind the victim and seizes him in the manner previously described. If the bottom is firm, the rescuer places his feet against it and shoves off for the surface. If it is weedy or muddy, the rescuer should swim up.

When the rescuer cannot locate the victim in the foregoing manner either because of general murkiness of the water or if it is after nightfall, a test surface dive is made. If the water is so deep that the rescuer finds it beyond his power to reach bottom, no further attempts should be made. He must then await the arrival of grappling apparatus. If, however, the water is of no great depth he should begin a series of systematic surface dives. Choosing the area he wishes to cover he should begin to dive at one side and cover the bottom in overlapping lanes across it until the body is located or until he satisfies himself that the victim is not in that section. The dives must be made easily and two or three body-lengths covered along the bottom after each one. The rescuer who strokes along the bottom for a considerable distance may locate the body if he is lucky but he quickly becomes exhausted by taxing himself in this manner. If he does not recover the victim in the first few attempts, he may be compelled to desist from his efforts long before the given area is completely searched.

Under conditions in which it is impossible to locate the victim by sight, the best procedure is to swim along about six inches above the bottom sweeping the hands ahead and to the sides in breast stroke fashion. It is surprising to note how frequently the victim can be located by this systematic groping.

If two or more good divers are present the area can be covered much more quickly and thoroughly if they dive covering the bottom in parallel lines and in formation, rather than haphazardly. When six divers work side by side with lanes slightly overlapping an area thirty feet in width can be covered in the same time that it takes one diver to cover a five foot path along the bottom.

Fig. 105. Picking up victim from bottom.

This method of rescue or recovery reaches its highest point of effectiveness in the mass formation surface dive. At places where large numbers of good swimmers and life savers are present when a person is reported missing they quickly join hands and spread along the beach opposite the swimming area. At a given signal they start walking into the water, searching the bottom with the feet until they reach neck-depth. At that point they start surface diving simultaneously and abreast. After each dive, they come up, move back a body length, realign the group and start the next one, working outward progressively until the victim is located or the entire area covered. In this way tremendous areas may be searched in a surprisingly short time and experience has proved that the victim can be recovered more quickly in this manner than in any other way.

The Water Glass.—The water glass or "water scope," as it is sometimes called, is a device used in clear water to scan the bottom and locate the victim. Even in very clear water, the refraction of light on the surface or the action of waves does not always permit an entirely clear view to the person looking for a victim or an object. To meet this condition, an adaptation of an old device used by sponge divers has been put to use. The sponge diver for many years was accustomed to using a bucket, the bottom of which was knocked out and replaced by a circular piece of glass, and made watertight. Hanging over the side or the stern of his boat, the sponger floated his bucket on the surface and peered into it. Its bottom being below the surface, refraction was eliminated and the diver was able to scan the marine life beneath him and locate sponges.

For the location of a victim on the bottom, the water glass in its present form offers some improvements over the glass-bottomed bucket. In shape, it is not unlike a four-sided megaphone made of wood. The large end, approximately a foot square, is grooved on the inner surface of the four sides about an inch from the edge. In this groove a square of glass is set in whiting or red lead to make it watertight. This four-sided box is eighteen inches high and narrows to an opening at the top approximately three by six inches. This opening is the eye piece and is so designed and shaped that it fits closely about the eyes to keep out light from above as the user looks down. The eye piece is of such width that it excludes the nose to avoid fogging the glass with the breath. A handle or grip is placed on each side, a little lower than midway of the length.

The water glass is used either off a low dock or float, if the object of search is somewhere beneath it, or over the stern of a rowboat if in open water. With the glass end submerged, the user can hold it by means of the handles and scan the bottom either while stationary or while an assistant rows along slowly over the area to be searched.

This piece of apparatus can also be used at night with a powerful flashlight. The light is held above the surface and directed downward outside the water scope. It is not satisfactory to suspend the light within the box as the reflection upon the glass obscures the vision.

Grappling.—Grappling devices should be considered as rescue equipment and as such should be available in some form for immediate use wherever people bathe or drowning accidents are likely to occur. While it is true that grappling irons have their greatest value in the recovery of bodies, it has frequently happened that victims have been recovered on the first cast of the irons in places where the water was too deep for surface dive recovery. If irons are accessible and in readiness for use it is sometimes possible to bring the victim to the surface in time to apply artificial respiration successfully.

Through the years many types of grappling apparatus have been devised and used with varying degrees of success. Some have been rigged to meet purely local conditions and because of this cannot be widely used. Two types of apparatus have been developed, however, which seem to meet all requirements for this type of rescue or body recovery.

In waters where the bottom is weed-grown, dotted with snags or covered with broken rock and boulders, only one device can be used with any degree of success.

This device which is used from a boat is a long pole (12 to 16 feet) to which is secured a single stout hook of three or four inch span. With it the body is located by systematic gentle probing and after it is discovered the hook is used to bring the victim's body to the surface. Practice in its use will enable a person to detect the difference in feeling of various substances quite hidden from view. Thus it can be determined in a remarkably short time whether the hook is in contact with rock, wood, weed masses or the body of a victim. A clothed dummy placed on the bottom is often used for practice.

To recover a victim in open water where the bottom is

comparatively free from obstructions, dragging with grappling irons is generally resorted to.

The best type of iron for this purpose is the bar or T iron made of ¾" galvanized iron pipe. The bar itself is four feet long and the stock is eighteen inches in length. At intervals of one foot, gangs of triple hooks are suspended by means of short pieces of stout line. A bridle of rope or galvanized iron wire is attached at one end of the drag bar, brought up and threaded through a hole in the upper end of the stock and made fast at the opposite end of the drag. At the top of the stock a ring is fixed and to it is attached a hundred feet of three-eighths inch line. Plumber's stock is used for the frame and the stock and bar are joined by a T-joint.

If the approximate spot where the victim sank is known, the irons are put overboard a little to one side of that spot and dragged swiftly but carefully across it. This may be done three or four times. If the victim is not caught in the first few tries, it is evident that he has been moved by currents or the spot was not accurately noted, so the rescuer must begin systematic dragging.

All dragging requires two men for the operation, one to row and the other to handle the irons, and systematic coverage of a given area requires close cooperation between rower and dragger. The oarsman is responsible for laying a course well to one side of the place where the victim was last seen. Sighting by some landmark on shore, he rows a straight course directly outward, then turning about he takes a parallel course back to the starting point. This process is repeated until the entire area has been thoroughly covered.

The "iron-tender" puts the irons over the stern and allows them to sink to the bottom. The line is then paid out sufficiently to allow the irons to be dragged at an angle of about 45° and the tender holds the line over the stern as though he were "trolling" for fish. When the hooks engage an object on the bottom and the line tautens, orders should immediately be given to rower to hold water, and then to back-water slowly as the tender brings the line in hand-over-hand, until the boat is directly above the irons. Carefully the tender begins to pull on the rope to determine what has been hooked. If the irons do not readily lift from the bottom it may be assumed that they are fouled on a submerged rock, log or snag and the boat should then be backed beyond the irons and turned about so that they may be manipulated free of the obstruction. If they are so securely hooked that they cannot be freed by manipulation, force must be exerted even to the point of breaking some of the hooks.

When the first pull indicates that something movable has been hooked the line should be brought in slowly and carefully and the irons lifted. As the irons come to the surface the tender can see what he has caught. If it is the victim, the tender should unhurriedly reach over and seize the arm or leg and, after free-ing the body of the hooks, lift it into the boat where resuscita-tion measures can be started at once, if indicated. If the irons bring up brush or weed, the hooks should be cleared as quickly as possible, the boat backed a bit more on its plotted course and the dragging operation resumed.

Body Recovery

It is a perfectly natural human trait to persist in trying to recover the body of a drowned person even though all hope of resuscitation may be gone. This slow and painful process may go on for days or even weeks before the body is recovered or all hope abandoned. Before the means used in this process are discussed it is well to review what happens to a body in drown-ing and what natural reactions may aid in its discovery.

It has been previously stated that a body settles to the bottom as soon as its specific gravity is greater than that of the water it displaces and that, unless it is caught and held by some obstruction, eventually it will rise to the surface again as soon as the gases formed by decomposition give it enough buoyancy to offset its weight. This is but partly true since we know that in many deep lakes where the water at the bottom is very cold bodies do not come to the surface again. This may be explained by the fact that the extremely low temperature of the water may act as a preserving factor by greatly retarding the processes of decomposition. Under such circumstances the body merely disintegrates in its final resting place. This accounts also for the fact that the bodies of persons drowned in northern lakes and streams during the winter months quite often are not found until spring or early summer after the water has become somewhat warmer.

Many vague ideas and superstitions have grown about this altogether natural process of bodies rising to the surface. These are far too numerous to list completely but a few may be cited to show that they have no basis in fact. Thus, it is said in some parts of the country that a body will rise with the waxing of the moon; in others, with its waning. In some sections it is solemnly averred that the victim will be found floating after the first warm rains. In some places bordering on the sea, it is stated as a fact that nothing but a "perigee" tide will bring up the body and it is almost universally believed that a severe thunderstorm will be the uplifting factor. All of these, and many others with two possible exceptions, have not a single scientific basis of fact to support them. In the main they are based wholly on coincidence. Thus, bodies have been found floating at both the waxing and the waning of the moon. Warm rains frequently occur in the spring months and are coincidental with the rising temperature of the water. The thunderstorm and the high tide may be real factors in bringing a body to the surface but by no magi-

cal means of electrical or hydrostatic force. The rumbling reverberation of thunder may loosen a body from the tenacious grip
of mud or silt by vibration and an extremely high tide can develop especially strong flowing currents along the bottom which
may accomplish the same thing.

Thus it may be seen that a body resting freely upon the
bottom may be expected under usual circumstances to return
to the surface. The number of hours or days it will take is dependent upon the temperature of the water and the consequent
rate of decomposition. If it does not appear within a reasonable time, it may be concluded that it is being held by some
obstruction.

In the early stages of any search for a body, dragging and
probing with grappling irons and hooks will be the usual means
employed. For careful combing of the bottom, the contour and
character of the lake or stream must first be studied and then a
definite course of action planned. A survey of the body of water in which the victim drowned should take into consideration
the extreme limits within which the victim may lie, the character of the bottom, if known, the location of snags and obstructions, the presence of currents, eddies and backwaters, everything as a matter of fact, which would have any influence
upon the movement or ultimate resting place of the body. The
area should then be blocked off in sections and a thorough
search made of each section before proceeding to the next one.

Even at its best and under the most favorable circumstances, dragging is a blind operation in which the body may be
passed over or close to, again and again during operations. Because of this, if the body is not found after the area has been
thoroughly dragged, it is advisable to obtain the services of a
professional diver. With diving dress and pumps it is possible for
him to walk over and scrutinize every foot of the bottom in the
drowning area, leaving no portions uninspected.

Dynamite has been used extensively in the past and its use will be continued in many instances for the purpose of "bringing up" bodies. Inasmuch as the use of high explosives is confined to those who by experience or profession are expert in handling it, it will not be discussed here except to state that it can sometimes be employed effectively to bring a body to the surface. There is no mysterious alchemy by which bodies react to the explosion of dynamite and ascend to the surface, as some would believe. By the reverberation of its explosion, a body may be shaken loose from the grip of mud, sand or silt and, if close enough, the force of the explosion may serve to tear it loose from a snag. If, however, decomposition is not far enough advanced to buoy the body to the surface it will only settle again in another resting place a few feet away. It can be seen then that the use of dynamite is most effective in the later stages of an extensive search.

CHAPTER VII

RESUSCITATION

The problem of saving a person's life in a near-drowning accident does not end when the rescue attempt is successfully completed and the victim brought to shore. Indeed, it is frequently merely the beginning of what may prove to be a long and involved process of maintaining life and restoring animation.

If the victim has suffered no more than a mere ducking during which he has swallowed some water and had a temporary scare, there is little to be done after he has been rescued except to assist him to shallow water or to shore. There he may rest and recover under the watchful eye of the rescuer and any tendency to panic and possible shock may be counteracted by minimizing the danger involved in the experience. After recovery the victim should be encouraged to go back into the water and play around for a time as a means of forgetting his recent unfortunate experience and to prevent the possible development of distaste for the water, or even fear.

When the victim is rescued, however, after a prolonged struggle to stay afloat, the condition may be much more serious even though he is brought to shore still breathing and conscious. Fear and extremely violent exertion have combined to put him in a state in which the heart is greatly weakened as a result of its extraordinary efforts and, if not actually in a state of collapse, the victim's physical and mental state may be such as to induce the condition soon thereafter.

There is only one rule governing the conduct of the rescuer to prevent possible failure of the weakened heart and that is to allow no further physical exertion by the victim. He must not be allowed to walk or even to stand erect unsupported. On one occasion in New York a man was rescued from the river. He was hauled to the deck of a nearby ship and as he stood offering his thanks to the rescuer, he suddenly collapsed, fell to the deck and died within a few moments. The rescuer should carry the victim to a resting place and insist upon having him lie down until pulse and respiration are more nearly normal.

Shock in Drowning.—It is suspected that shock develops in almost every near-drowning experience. The degree of shock depends largely upon the victim's mental and, to a lesser extent, physical reaction to the situation he is in or from which he has just escaped. It may vary all the way from a mere feeling of faintness to unconsciousness and death. Because it may develop progressively from the initial state to one of extreme severity and danger, its manifestations must be recognized and dealt with correctly if a life is to be saved.

What actually happens in shock is not known but apparently that part of the nervous system which regulates the flow of blood loses its control over the blood vessels. These in turn relax and allow the blood to stagnate, chiefly in the small blood vessels and capillaries of the abdomen. The circulation in veins and arteries is greatly reduced and blood pressure is lowered. The skin, arms and legs, the brain, and even the heart receive an insufficient supply of blood for their needs and function only partially or not at all.

Signs of shock are well known and are readily apparent even to the untrained eye, although the connection between signs and conditions may not always be recognized. In slight shock there may be pallor, more rapid pulse, and a general feeling of weakness from which the victim can usually recover after a little rest. Nausea and sometimes vomiting may develop if the shock is a little more severe. Too often in the past has the nausea of a drowning victim been supposed to have resulted from the water he swallowed when it is more likely that it was a direct result of shock.

Severe shock is very serious and must be recognized and treated quickly or death is likely to result. Many of the signs appearing in slight shock are present here. The pallor of the face, the rapid and weak pulse, nausea and general weakness are supplemented by irregular breathing (long, deep, sighing breaths alternate with very shallow ones). The body may feel cold and clammy and a severe chill may set in with violent shaking and chattering teeth. If conscious, the victim may be lying inert with eyes fixed in a vacant glassy stare. In his feeble movements and rapt inattention to what is going on about him, he seems to be partly in the other world even before life processes have ceased.

A person in a state of severe shock needs medical attention as soon as it can be obtained, but meanwhile he cannot wait upon the doctor's arrival and survive unless something is done to alleviate the condition. This is where knowledge of first aid is of great value. First aid in cases of severe shock is based upon position, heat, and fluids.

Because the brain and heart are suffering from a deficiency of blood, the victim is placed in a near-horizontal position, with the head 12 to 18 inches lower than the feet; i.e., with the head toward the water. This position will permit gravity-flow of the blood to the parts where it is most needed.

In shock there is a rapid loss of body heat. To check this loss the victim should be swathed in blankets, coats, or articles of similar nature. He should be protected underneath as well as above. Friction of arms and legs is of doubtful value in cases of shock.

Fluids have some value in shock. Plain water, neither hot nor cold, is the best fluid. If there will be delay until medical care is available, administer a few sips at first. Observe the patient's tolerance and thirst, and increase the amount to a half glass at a time if the victim can swallow. But in no case should any attempt be made to force it down the throat of an unconscious person. No alcohol should be used. This marks the limit of the application of first aid to a victim of shock. Further treatment is within the province of the doctor, and the victim should not be moved except at his direction.

Unconsciousness.—It happens frequently that the victim of a water accident is found to be unconscious when taken from the water. This may have been the result of the struggle to stay afloat, a blow on the head, heart failure, apoplexy, or exhaustion from prolonged immersion. It may range in seriousness from fainting to complete collapse. If the victim has stopped breathing, artificial respiration must be resorted to. It should not be applied while the victim is still breathing unless it is apparent that respiration is about to cease.

If the victim has merely fainted, the face will be pale, the breathing shallow, and the pulse weak. First aid in this case consists of placing the person in an inclined position with the head somewhat lower than the feet. Garments should be loosened—especially about the neck. Until recovery is complete, the victim should be covered with a blanket or coat and remain lying.

Unconsciousness resulting from an actual drowning experience requires the rescuer to place the victim in a reclining position (preferably on the right side) and cover him with blankets or coats. Inasmuch as respiration may cease while the person is in this condition, the rescuer should stand by in readiness to use artificial respiration. Rest and warmth are the two best aids to recovery.

Head or spine injuries that result in unconsciousness occur most frequently in diving. The victim may have struck the diving board, some portion of the diving structure, a floating or submerged obstruction, or the bottom. There is usually little doubt about this kind of water accident; either someone sees it take place, or the circumstances in which the victim is found indicate what has happened.

Great care should be taken in recovering the victim from the water. If the vertebrae of the neck or back are cracked or displaced a very little, further displacement may injure the spinal cord and paralysis or death ensue. From deep water the victim must, of course, be taken in a cross chest carry; but when shallow water is reached, methods other than the usual one of taking him ashore must be devised. If a surfboard, plank, or stretcher is available, it should be brought out and floated beneath the injured person and he should be carried ashore upon it. If no device of this kind is immediately available, the victim should be floated into shallow water until he grounds at the water edge. As long as the water is not rough and the face is clear to permit breathing, the victim can rest there quite comfortably until suitable means for transportation can be obtained.

Breaks and dislocations of the spine can be recognized frequently by a certain definite deformity and evidence of localized pain. The neck may be twisted or bent to an unnatural angle; the spine may be distorted. No attempt should be made to straighten or align the parts. Victims who have suffered spinal injury should be left lying inert in a level position until they can be cared for by a doctor.

All head injuries resulting from a blow should be regarded as serious whether or not the scalp is split or torn and even if the victim recovers consciousness within a few moments. Often fracture of the skull and concussion of the brain are not recognized immediately and may cause death if the victim is allowed to resume activity. Bleeding from the ears generally indicates fracture at base of skull. The victim should be kept in a reclining position and should not be moved unless absolutely necessary until he has been seen by a doctor. The victim should be kept warm and no stimulants should be given. If the face is normal in color or flushed, the head should be raised; otherwise, it is allowed to remain level.

Heart failure is a common occurrence among bathers, especially among those who are getting along in years, and is due generally to overexertion or excitement. It is frequently marked by collapse without warning and often the victim is discovered floating face-down in the very midst of a group of bathers. Contrary to popular belief, it is not always fatal; but the outcome of an attack often depends upon the manner in which the victim is handled.

It must be determined immediately upon bringing the victim to shore if he has ceased to breathe. Artificial respiration is, of course, resorted to in such case. If unconscious but still breathing, the victim is placed in a reclining position and covered sufficiently to keep warm. If and when consciousness is restored, the victim should be kept quiet, except in one instance. If he complains that he cannot breathe in the reclining position, he should be propped up. In some forms of heart disease the victim is more comfortable so. Regardless of the severity of the attack, a physician should always be summoned.

Attacks of apoplexy and epilepsy occur occasionally while bathing. Epileptics are generally known in a community and if they go swimming are likely to be accompanied by persons who know how to handle them. In case of attack, the epileptic is taken from the water, placed in a reclining position, and covered to keep warm. A plug of wood wrapped in a cloth is inserted between the teeth to prevent the victim from chewing and injuring the tongue.

Apoplexy (stroke) usually attacks persons past 50 years of age and offers as its most characteristic symptoms a flushed and engorged face and neck, and snoring breathing. The victim is placed on the back with head and shoulders raised, covered for warmth, and may have cold cloths or ice packs applied to the head. A physician should be summoned.

Respiratory Failure.—No matter what the cause may have been, artificial respiration is applied to those taken from the water who have stopped breathing. Only in two cases are exceptions made to this rule; first, if the person is obviously dead and second, if the victim has been under water for a period of several hours or days. In all other cases, no attempt is made to diagnose the condition. Heart failure, shock, apoplexy, or drowning may be the physician's diagnosis later on, but at the moment only one method of treatment is indicated to the person rendering first aid and that is artificial respiration.

The Respiratory Tract.—For better understanding of what takes place when a person drowns, it is advisable to know a little of the anatomy of the respiratory tract. At its upper end, there are three openings that readily admit air—the mouth and the nostrils. These communicate through two chambers (pharynx and larynx) with a passage in the throat known as the trachea, or windpipe, which in turn leads downward to the lungs. The lungs, themselves, are not simply bags into which air is drawn but are made up of great numbers of tiny cells (alveoli). The windpipe divides before reaching the lungs into two branches (bronchi); and when these enter the lungs, they divide and subdivide into smaller and smaller branches until there is a tiny ventilating pipe reaching every cluster of air cells. The arrangement is not unlike multiple branches of very tiny grapes all growing in two great clusters. Paralleling the trachea and just behind it is another tube (the esophagus), down which food and drink pass to the stomach. Because the upper ends of these passages open into the throat, the processes of eating, drinking, and breathing would be very complicated if it were not for the fact that nature has provided a singularly simple but effective mechanism for closing the windpipe while food or drink is being swallowed. This is a flap known as the epiglottis, which is so sensitive that it will allow nothing but air or a gas to pass it. When solids or liquids come into contact with the epiglottis, it closes down tightly over the upper end of the wind-pipe and will not release readily until the substance has passed on into the esophagus. It is true that occasionally the epiglottis is caught unawares and food or liquid does get a little way into the windpipe. When this happens it goes into spasm and holds until the substance is coughed out. This may happen for in-stance when one is eating and talking or laughing at the same time.

Certain muscles of the chest walls and the diaphragm, con-trolled by a nerve center in one portion of the brain, act in concert to permit inhalation of air into the lungs and to expel it.

With an understanding of the mechanism involved, it is possible to see why and how a person drowns.

When a victim drowns passively, that is, when he loses consciousness with little or no struggle, he is very quickly as-phyxiated because the water simply shuts off his air supply. An actively drowning victim, however, presents a very different aspect. If not already in a vertical position, he will arrive at one very quickly as the legs cease to make controlled move-ments. Panic increases and arm-strokes, which were sustaining his progress, are now directed vertically. Alternately the head is lifted above and dropped below the surface and in his des-perate, irregular gasps for air he takes in much water. The epi-glottis closes and opens spasmodically responding to the touch of the inrushing water. Much of the water is swallowed. Chok-ing and coughing, the victim loses tidal air with every cough and sinks lower and lower. Even when the head appears above the water the epiglottis may still be in spasm and he will be able to get little or no air. The muscles of the arms and shoulders tire quickly and the movements become more and more feeble and uncontrolled. The brain, deprived of its customary supply of oxygen, begins to lose its function. All effort to breathe stops, motion ceases, and the victim sinks downward finally to rest inert on the bottom.

For a brief interval the victim may remain conscious and for a longer time, varying with every individual, the heart may continue to beat and life processes go on. The hapless individual, however, may be said to have entered that twilight zone between life and death known as suspended animation, and death may ensue at any moment.

This then is the situation that confronts the rescuer when he brings an apparently drowned person ashore. The victim is unconscious, has ceased to breathe, and life may or may not be extinct. There is no simple means of knowing within the knowledge of the average individual. The stomach is filled with water and there may or may not be water in the lungs (that is unimportant). The victim's body is wet and the evaporation of water on the skin is already at work reducing the temperature of the body and making death all the more certain. Something must be done and done quickly to prolong life if it is still present and to restore the victim. Artificial respiration and supplementary first aid measures are indicated as vitally necessary.

History of Artificial Respiration.—From earliest times mankind has seen and contemplated the fact of violent death as hideous and dreadful, to be shunned as something the shadow of which might fall upon those who viewed its victims. Death with one of the elements as its cause, fire, earth, air, or water, was difficult to understand and greatly to be feared. This fear of the incomprehensible has persisted down through the ages to this very day among more primitive peoples, and even the unenlightened and ignorant of so-called civilized nations are still governed to some extent by fear and superstition in their attitude toward victims of accident. Thus there may be found in any crowd that gathers at the scene of a drowning many persons who cannot be prevailed upon to try to revive or even to touch the apparently lifeless person. That this is due in large measure to lack of knowledge of means of resuscitation is undeniable, but it is nonetheless true that fear and superstition not infrequently contribute to their inaction.

Fortunately, however, all through history there have been men of courage and wisdom who have refused to accept the fact of death as visited upon victims of the water. With compassionate eyes they have viewed the unfortunates and noted that those recently drowned looked much the same as other men except that they were unconscious and did not breathe. In their wisdom these men had the courage to try to restore life by artificially induced respiration, often against adverse popular opinion. As late as the year 1794, according to Ralph Thomas, resuscitation as advocated by Dr. Hawes, founder of the Royal Humane Society, was considered "impious and placed nearly upon a level with professing to raise the dead."

The ancient history of ways of restoring life by artificial means is very meager, yet an indication of knowledge of a method is found in Genesis, where it is written that "God formed man of the dust of the ground and breathed into his nostrils the breath of life; and man became a living soul." This would seem to indicate that Moses, to whom the book of Genesis is attributed, had knowledge of a means of restoring life which has been and is being used occasionally even to this day.

Prior to the eighteenth century the practice of breathing into the nostrils in the Biblical manner was undoubtedly employed in attempting to revive apparently drowned persons. To better perform this operation some genius whose name is not known contrived a small bellows to be inserted in the nostril to inflate the lungs in a more hygienic manner. At some time in the late Middle Ages the practice of rolling a drowned person across a cask came into use, as did the practice of suspension by the heels. Bleeding was very commonly employed as, at one time, it was considered a panacea for nearly all ills.

When Dr. Hawes founded the Royal Humane Society in 1774, he set himself to the tasks (1) of combating ignorance and superstition, (2) of investigating and discrediting the inadequate methods aforementioned which he found in use, and (3) of evolving newer and better ways of resuscitating the apparently drowned. Again, Ralph Thomas is cited as authority for the impression that Dr. Hawes turned away from the principle of inducing respiration artificially to one of preserving life by the application of heat.

With the methods advocated by Dr. Hawes and the Royal Humane Society and the older practices of the use of the bellows, cask rolling, suspension by the heels, and blood-letting, which persisted in spite of Dr. Hawes' condemnation, humanity struggled along until 1856 when Dr. Marshall Hall set forth the principle of artificial respiration by pressure on the walls of the thorax. His method of combined rolling from prone to side position and pressure on the back was followed quickly by that of Silvester in 1857. Silvester placed the victim on the back and applied pressure to the front of the chest wall. The adaptations of Dr. Howard in the United States and Dr. Bowles in England followed and were used to some extent by the lifesaving and humane societies of the two countries. Each method in its turn seemed to have improved upon the one immediately preceding it, but they were all only partially effective and left much to be desired.

In 1903, Dr. E. Sharpey Schafer, an English physician, devised another method of applying artificial respiration which for a number of years was used almost to the exclusion of older methods. This became known as the Schafer method or, more simply and descriptively, the prone pressure method. It was introduced in the United States in 1907. At first it was received somewhat skeptically, but gradually it became the most generally accepted method and was almost universally taught and used until 1951.

In 1935 Colonel Holger Nielsen, a Dane, developed still another manual method of artificial respiration which he introduced in Denmark. It became known in the United States not long thereafter. Colonel Nielsen's method appeared at first to be made up of elements from several previously devised methods. Furthermore, it resembled at least one or two older methods that had been given up some time before because they were too tiring for the operator to use for more than a few minutes. The Neilsen method however not only appeared to give excellent ventilation of the lungs but it was easy to learn and perform. Its use was extended steadily in Europe; nevertheless, it did not at first find ready acceptance in the United States.

During the late 1940s considerable research in the use and effectiveness of manual methods of resuscitation was undertaken in the United States at the behest of the Department of Defense. Some military medical experts felt that the almost universally taught Schafer method did not get good results in some types of asphyxia. At about this same time the American Red Cross became interested in the problem and sponsored in part a research project at the University of Illinois medical school in which several of the better methods of artificial respiration were tested, compared for effectiveness, and evaluated.

In October 1951 a meeting of experts, authorities, and interested persons was held at the National Research Council in Washington, D.C. As a result of this meeting it was recommended that the Holger-Neilsen method (one of those tested and evaluated) with certain modification be adopted since tests proved conclusively that better and deeper ventilation of the lungs was obtained with it than with any other method. For ease of identification and as a descriptive name it was recommended that it be known as the back pressure-arm lift method of artificial respiration.

Research in artificial respiration continued. In 1958 the National Academy of Sciences-National Research Council Ad Hoc Committee on Artificial Respiration reviewed the data on artificial respiration obtained through research projects supported by the Department of the Army, the American Red Cross, and others.

It was unanimously agreed by members of the committee that the mouth-to-mouth (or mouth-to-nose) technique of artificial respiration is the most practical method for emergency ventilation of an individual of any age who has stopped breathing, in the absence of equipment or of help from a second person, regardless of the cause of cessation of breathing.

First aid-trained people do not usually have the experience, training, and essential equipment to distinguish whether or not lack of breathing is a result of disease or accident. **Therefore, some form of artificial respiration should be started at the earliest possible moment.**

Any procedure that will obtain and maintain an open air passageway from the lungs to the mouth and provide for an alternate increase and decrease in the size of the chest, internally or externally, will move air in and out of a nonbreathing person.

The mouth-to-mouth (or mouth-to-nose) technique has the advantage of providing pressure to inflate the victim's lungs immediately. It also enables the rescuer to obtain more accurate information on the volume, pressure, and timing of efforts needed to inflate the victim's lungs than is afforded by other methods.

This is, in brief, a history of the efforts men have made to devise manual life-restoring methods for apparently drowned persons. Two developments should be noted. First, in modern times it was recognized that the methods could be used in almost all cases of asphyxia. Each in its turn, therefore, was used not only in case of drowning but also in asphyxia due to electric shock, gas poisoning, and some forms of mechanical suffocation. Second, paralleling the evolution of manual methods, especially during the last several decades, there has been a progressive development of devices to perform artificial respiration mechanically or to make manual methods more effective. These mechanical devices fall into three classifications: respirators, inhalators, and resuscitators. The respirator effects an exchange of air by alternately building up air pressure on the victim's chest walls and then releasing it. The respirator is a piece of hospital apparatus used most frequently for paralyzed polio patients. An inhalator is a simple tank and face mask device that administers oxygen, or a mixture of oxygen and carbon dioxide, to the victim as artificial respiration is applied. Since it is not constructed to exert positive pressure sufficient to inflate the lungs, it is used with the manual method of artificial respiration. The resuscitator is a purely mechanical device for alternately inflating and deflating the lungs. It does not need the application of a manual method to make it work, although in some types the flow of oxygen from the tank can be controlled so that they may be used as inhalators if desired.

Inhalators and resuscitators are portable so that they may be brought to the scene of a drowning accident. To await the arrival of a machine, however, is almost certain to mean death to the victim, since a delay of even seconds may sometimes be fatal. The skilled hands of the rescuer are immediately available. They should, therefore, be put to work at once. Unless the rescuer or the first aider has had special training he should not attempt to use an inhalator or a resuscitator. Usually the machine will be accompanied by a person trained in its use.

When a person is unconscious and not breathing, the base of the tongue tends to press against and block the upper air passageway. The procedures described below should provide for an open air passageway when a lone rescuer must perform artificial respiration.

Mouth-to-mouth (Mouth-to-nose) Method of Artificial Respiration

If there is foreign matter visible in the mouth, wipe it out quickly with your fingers or a cloth wrapped around your fingers.

1. Tilt the head back so the chin is pointing upward (A). Pull or push the jaw into a jutting-out position (B and C).

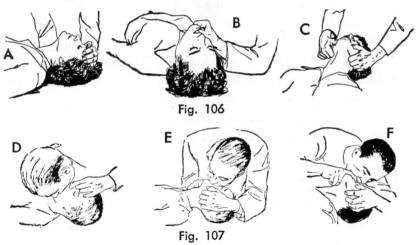

Fig. 106

Fig. 107

These maneuvers should relieve obstruction of the airway by moving the base of the tongue away from the back of the throat.

2. Open your mouth wide and place it tightly over the victim's mouth. At the same time pinch the victim's nostrils shut (D) or close the nostrils with your cheek (E). Or close the victim's mouth and place your mouth over the nose (F). Blow into the victim's mouth or nose. (Air may be blown through the victim's teeth, even though they may be clenched.)

The first blowing efforts should determine whether or not obstruction exists.

3. Remove your mouth, turn your head to the side, and listen for the return rush of air that indicates air exchange. Repeat the blowing effort.

   For an adult, blow vigorously at the rate of about 12 breaths per minute. For a child, take relatively shallow breaths appropriate for the child's size, at the rate of about 20 per minute.

4. If you are not getting air exchange, recheck the head and jaw position (A, B, and C). If you still do not get air exchange, quickly turn the victim on his side and administer several sharp blows between the shoulder blades in the hope of dislodging foreign matter (G).

G

Fig. 108

Again sweep your fingers through the victim's mouth to remove foreign matter.

Those who do not wish to come in contact with the person may hold a cloth over the victim's mouth or nose and breathe through it. The cloth does not greatly affect the exchange of air.

Mouth-to-mouth Technique for Infants and Small Children

If foreign matter is visible in the mouth, clean it out quickly as described previously.

1. Place the child on his back and use the fingers of both hands to lift the lower jaw from beneath and behind, so that it juts out (A).

2. Place your mouth over the child's mouth AND nose, making a relatively leakproof seal, and breathe into

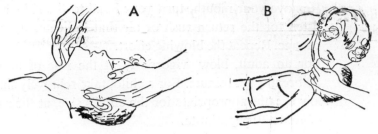

Fig. 109

the child, using shallow puffs of air (B). The breathing rate should be about 20 per minute.

If you meet resistance in your blowing efforts, recheck the position of the jaw. If the air passages are still blocked, the child should be suspended momentarily by the ankles (C) or inverted over one arm (D) and given two or three sharp pats between the shoulder blades, in the hope of dislodging obstructing matter.

Fig. 110

Manual Methods of Artificial Respiration

Rescuers who cannot, or will not, use mouth-to-mouth or mouth-to-nose techniques, should use a manual method. The rescuer should not be limited to the use of a single manual method for all cases, since the nature of the injury in any given case may prevent the use of one method, while favoring another.

It has already been pointed out that the base of the tongue tends to press against and block the air passage when a person is unconscious and not breathing. *This action of the tongue can occur whether the victim is in a face-down or face-up position.*

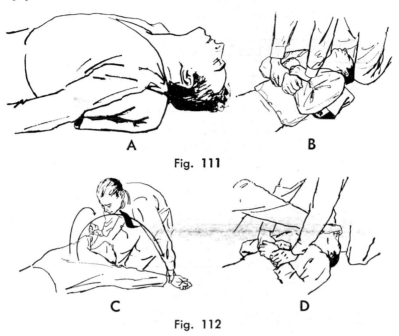

A B

Fig. 111

C D

Fig. 112

The Chest Pressure-Arm Lift (Silvester) Method

If there is foreign matter visible in the mouth, wipe it out quickly with your fingers or a cloth wrapped around your fingers.

1. Place the victim in a face-up position and put something under his shoulders to raise them and allow the head to drop backward (A).
2. Kneel at the victim's head, grasp his arms at the wrists, cross them, and press them over the lower chest (B). This should cause air to flow out.
3. Immediately release this pressure and pull the arms outward and upward over his head and backward as far as possible (C). This should cause air to rush in.

4. Repeat this cycle about 12 times per minute, checking the mouth frequently for obstructions.

When the victim is in a face-up position, there is always danger of aspiration of vomitus, blood, or blood clots. This hazard can be reduced by keeping the head extended and turned to one side. If possible, the head should be a little lower than the trunk.

If a second rescuer is available, have him hold the victim's head so that the jaw is jutting out (D).

The helper should be alert to detect the presence of any stomach contents in the mouth and keep the mouth as clean as possible at all times.

The Back Pressure-Arm Lift (Holger-Nielsen) Method

If there is foreign matter visible in the mouth, wipe it out quickly with your fingers or a cloth wrapped around your fingers.

1. Place the victim face-down, bend his elbows and place his hands one upon the other, turn his head slightly to one side and extend it as far as possible, making sure that the chin is jutting out (A).

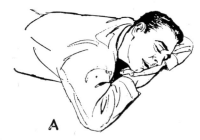
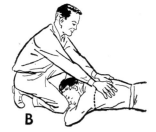

Fig. 113

Fig. 114

2. Kneel at the head of the victim. Place your hands on the flat of the victim's back so that the palms lie just below an imaginary line running between the armpits (B).

3. Rock forward until the arms are approximately vertical and allow the weight of the upper part of your body to exert steady, even pressure downward upon the hands (C).

4. Immediately draw his arms upward and toward you, applying enough lift to feel resistance and tension at his shoulders (D). Then lower the arms to the ground. Repeat this cycle about 12 times per minute, checking the mouth frequently for obstruction.

If a second rescuer is available, have him hold the victim's head so that the jaw continues to jut out (E). The helper should be alert to detect any stomach contents in the mouth and keep the mouth as clean as possible at all times.

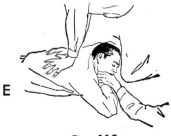

Fig. 115

Artificial Respiration for Water Cases

Individuals who die as a result of a water accident usually die from the lack of air, and not because of water in the lungs or stomach.

A drowning victim may be either active or passive. Unless unconscious, the drowning victim usually struggles to remain on the surface or to regain the surface, in order to secure air. These efforts are energy-consuming and may result in the victim swallowing varying quantities of water. This water, along with food remaining in the stomach, could, if regurgitated, obstruct the air passages and interfere with the efforts of the rescuer. The possibility of obstruction must be recognized by the rescuer and immediate steps taken to relieve it if it occurs.

Evaporation of water from the victim's skin will result in lowering still further a body temperature that may already be dangerously low. It is imperative, therefore, to keep the victim from becoming chilled.

Related Information for All Artificial Respiration Methods

Time your efforts to coincide with the victim's first attempt to breathe for himself.

If vomiting occurs, quickly turn the victim on his side, wipe out his mouth, and then reposition him.

Normally, recovery should be rapid, except in electric shock, drug poisoning, or carbon monoxide poisoning cases. In these instances, nerves and muscles controlling the breathing system are paralyzed or deeply depressed, or the carbon monoxide has displaced oxygen in the blood stream over a period of time. When these cases are encountered, artificial respiration must often be carried on for long periods.

Artificial respiration should be continued until the victim begins to breathe for himself, until a physician pronounces him dead, or until he appears to be dead beyond any doubt.

Condition of an Apparently Drowned Person

When an apparently drowned person is brought out of the water, no one can possibly know how long he may live without oxygen. It may be only a few seconds. It is important, there-fore, that no time at all be wasted before beginning artificial respiration. The question as to how long the victim was sub-merged is of little importance unless it is a matter of 2 or 3 hours or more since he disappeared beneath the surface. After such a length of time artificial respiration is not likely to be effective.

If the person who applies artificial respiration did not see the accident occur he should pay little attention to what bystand-ers say concerning the length of time the victim was under wa-ter. Eyewitness accounts are seldom reliable because of emo-tional reaction to the tragedy. An emotionally affected eyewit-ness may state that the victim sank to the bottom a half hour before, when the time may actually have been only 2 or 3 min-utes.

Complications may be caused by mud or sand blocking the mouth and nose or clothing binding and constricting the throat. All of these factors must be considered, of course, but the victim's need for oxygen must take precedence over every-thing else.

Another complication in the resuscitation of an appar-ently drowned person is the fact that the victim's body and clothing are wet. Even on a warm day there is likely to be con-stant evaporation of the water on or against the skin. This evap-oration will tend to accelerate chilling and to reduce the tem-perature of the body. It is important, therefore, to keep the vic-tim from becoming chilled.

Bystanders should be encouraged to assist. In the summer-time it will help if they do nothing more than dry the victim's body thoroughly. If possible, however, the victim should be cov-ered with blankets, coats, dry towels, or similar articles. If the victim is lying on a beach, it will help to heap hot sand along his sides and over his legs. The victim's chances of recovery are enhanced by such means; and even if he does not revive, certainly they will have done no harm.

The person trained in the use of artificial respiration should be able to recognize signs of returning animation if for no other reason than the encouragement they offer.

When a victim is brought from the water apparently lifeless, his face may be cyanotic (blue-black) or it may be pale, depending upon the degree of suffocation he endured. While artificial respiration is being applied, the appearance of the face may not change for some time. When the treatment begins to take effect, however, changes can be noted. The cyanosis, if present, may begin to fade; and if the victim is fair-skinned, it may be succeeded by a distinct flush of healthy color. This flush usually indicates that the heart is beginning to beat strongly once more. In many instances it is possible to detect a strengthening pulse before the victim actually starts to breathe for himself. Sometimes the mouth will begin to twitch, or the fingertips to creep. The most encouraging sign, however, occurs when a sobbing catch is heard during the inspiration of air. This may be followed by a groan and a series of gasping irregular breaths. At this point, the operator should watch carefully to be sure that he is not working against the victim's efforts to breathe for himself. As soon as the victim is breathing somewhat regularly of his own volition, the operator should cease artificial respiration.

Aftercare of the Victim

When the victim of a near-drowning is revived, he should not be allowed to get to his feet, get dressed, and go home. Until he is breathing regularly, he should be kept covered and remain where he is. If an ambulance arrives, or if for some other reason it is advisable for him to be moved, he should be carried on a stretcher, in an improvised blanket stretcher, or in the arms of two or three persons. If he is taken to an emergency room, to a hospital, or to his home, a doctor should be summoned to check on his condition. Usually, all the revived person requires is warmth and rest. He should not, however, be left alone for some hours because of the possibility of relapse or of complications setting in.

One who applies artificial respiration must back it with more than the usual amount of patience, courage, and fortitude. His faith in its life-restoring effects should always remain unshaken. He must be prepared to continue its use on a victim long after physical exhaustion prompts him to quit. Even if conditions appear hopeless, he cannot cease his efforts until he has no doubt that the victim is beyond human aid. He should face the fact that in many cases all his efforts will not restore life. He must not listen to the self-appointed advisers in the crowd that gathers, whose suggestions are neither timely nor accurate. Also, there are times—much less frequent now than in the past—when the trained life saver must stand by, restrained by some local authority, while less effective measures—or no efforts at all—are made to revive the victim. This is a burden that has to be borne.

A cool head and a calm, sure precision of movement command the respect of all in an emergency, and these are the best assets the life saver can possess. There may come a time in the experience of any life saver when he must acknowledge that all his efforts to revive the victim have been unavailing. Another time may come when his efforts are successful, and the victim breathes again. Whether successful or unsuccessful, the operator can take comfort in the knowledge that, if he did his work skillfully, he has done all that could be done in the best way that man has yet devised.

CHAPTER VIII

SPECIAL FORMS OF RESCUE

Boat Rescue

For anyone who has little or no skill in swimming rescue methods, the rowboat offers the best means of making any rescue of a victim (or victims) who is too far away to be reached by life rings or lines. The only preliminary requirement is that the rescuer should have some skill in handling the oars and maneuvering the boat. The life saver skilled in swimming rescue will use a boat by preference if one is readily accessible no matter what distance the victim may be from shore. The only exception will be when the victim is in such distress within a reasonable distance of shore that literally no time can be wasted in going to his assistance. The problem of whether to use a boat or to swim to the rescue must depend for solution upon the judgment of the rescuer and the time factors involved. For rescue of victims more than a hundred yards offshore a boat if available should always be used even if a little more time is taken to get it, launch and proceed to the rescue, than would be required to swim the same distance. Persons who get into difficulty some distance from shore are usually fair swimmers or they would not be there and they can be counted upon usually to sustain themselves on the surface for a little longer time than the novice swimmer. Others who get into difficulty well offshore are most generally thrown into the water as a result of capsizing a boat or canoe. Many of these victims manage to get a hand-hold on the overturned craft and are thus enabled to remain on the surface for some time. For the few non-swimmers who are pitched into the water and are unable to reach the craft from which they were thrown, complete submersion will be a matter of but a minute or two. A swimming rescuer under such circumstances will be of little assistance to the victim. His efforts in swimming speedily to the rescue will quite unfit him for the task of surface diving and he will be able to do little more than hold to the capsized craft until a rescue boat arrives.

Approaching by Boat.—The same problem occurs in going to a drowning victim by boat as in swimming to him. The fact that the victim may disappear beneath the surface at any moment makes it imperative to keep the gaze fixed upon him, or if he goes down, upon the spot at which he was last seen. The rowing approach is complicated by the fact that the oarsman in ordinary rowing position faces *away* from his objective.

If the rower is alone in the boat one of two courses is open to him in making the approach. If the distance to be covered is short, he may row out stern foremost facing the victim by employing the same stroke used in backing. If the distance is great and speed is imperative, he must row in the usual fashion and check his direction by frequent glances over his shoulder. Salt-water fishermen in their highsided dories use a form of rowing in tending seine or picking up lobster pots which permits constant forward vision while steady progress is made. The fisherman stands in his dory facing the bow, pushes the oars through the water and recovers them in a short choppy stroke. If the rescuer is practiced in this kind of rowing, it can well be used in making a long approach.

Whenever possible another person should go along in the stern sheets of the boat to guide and direct the rower and later to assist in picking up the victim.

Use of Cross Bearings.—For the rescue of a victim drowning at a considerable distance from shore, the use of cross bearings will be found to aid greatly in fixing the location of the victim even if he goes to the bottom. The practice of determining position by cross bearings is one of the oldest of navigational devices but its application to life saving is new.

When the swimmer in distress is sighted offshore, one person drops down on the shore and using a fishing rod, a spare oar or a boathook points it at the victim and sights along its length. Another person seizes a similar instrument and dashes off along the shore for a distance of a hundred or a hundred and fifty yards, where he drops to the sand, lines his pole or oar on the victim and sights along it. A boat is launched meanwhile from the first point and moves out along the first line of sight, being directed in its course by sighter number one. No attention is paid to the victim by the rescuer in the boat who devotes all his energies to rowing his course as directed. The victim meanwhile may have disappeared. The second sighter does not move until the boat crosses his line of vision when he jumps to his feet and waves his arms to indicate that the rescuer should cease rowing. At that point where the two lines of vision cross, the victim is located. An anchor is put over and by diving or grappling the victim is found and brought to the surface.

Effecting the Rescue.—As the boat nears the victim, a quick glance will suffice to indicate how the rescuer will make contact. It is of first importance that the rescuer should offer a handhold and support to the victim at the earliest possible moment. The question is, what are the circumstances and what will be the safest course to pursue?

If the victim is clinging to a capsized boat or canoe, time may be taken to reverse the rescue boat and back the transom (stern) within the victim's reach. If the wind is fair and a good sea running as is likely to be the case in a capsizing, the rescuer should reverse his boat and back it toward the victim from the **downwind** side. Riding in from the upwind side may cause the victim to be caught and crushed between the lunging craft.

When the victim happens to be an exhausted swimmer or one borne away from land by adverse currents which he cannot combat, the rescuer should turn his boat about and back down to the victim allowing him to grasp the transom.

An actively struggling victim, in mortal terror of losing his life, may make it necessary for the rescuer to glide in alongside and just out of reach, where an unshipped oar can be thrust blade foremost into his grasp. The victim may be completely submerged and still grasp the proffered oar if it is thrust into his hands. With it he can then be lifted slightly until the head is above water and swung around to the stern of the boat.

The feebly moving or unconscious victim cannot, of course, aid himself in any way. He is in momentary danger of disappearing beneath the surface. No time can be wasted in

Fig. 116. Using oar to aid victim.

reversing the boat or fishing with an oar. The rescuer simply comes alongside and after boating the nearside oar, leans over the side and seizes the victim. As soon as the head is above the surface, the rescuer unships the other oar and moves astern with the victim preparatory to bringing him into the boat.

When the victim slips beneath the surface just before or just as the rescue boat reaches him, time can be taken only to boat the oars, before the rescuer (provided he has had swimming rescue training), dives from the boat a little to one side of the spot where the victim was last seen and pursues him downward. The rescuer should stand squarely in the bottom of the boat and do a jackknife dive over the side, thrusting downward but as little backward as possible as he springs, to avoid pushing the boat beyond reach when he returns to the surface. In a fair breeze, an empty boat will drift faster than a man carrying a victim can swim. If it can be remembered to bring the rescue boat on the upwind side of the victim before diving, the craft will drift down within reach of the rescuer when he returns to the surface. If the boat drifts out of reach and is moving away rapidly, no time or energy should be spent in trying to overhaul it. A half dozen strokes in its direction will demonstrate whether it can be caught. Any portion of the boat may be grasped by the rescuer upon his return to the surface but as soon as possible he must work his way to the stern preparatory to getting the victim into the craft. The difficulty of keeping the boat in position while diving will be obviated if an anchor is a part of the equipment. It is the work of but a moment to heave it overside before diving.

When a victim disappears beneath the surface several minutes before the rescuer brings his boat to the scene, and if the exact point of disappearance has not been noted, a little more time can be taken to anchor the boat and to size up the situation. The rescuer who lacks swimming rescue knowledge and training should endeavor to locate the person by peering overside and probing with oar or boathook. The trained life saver, if the water is not too deep, can begin a series of surface dives in an effort to find the victim.

Getting the Victim into the Boat.—Few ordinary row-boats are broad enough of beam to bring a victim in over the side without capsizing or at least filling it with water. A terror-stricken drowning person can, if permitted to secure a grip upon the gunwale, press it under water and fill the craft in a trice. But give him a handhold upon the stern of the boat and no amount of pressing and scrambling will push it under water. This is why the point of entry is usually at the stern of a square-end boat. (Double-enders like the Adirondack guide boat are handled in rescue work like canoes.)

If the victim is conscious and capable of aiding himself to some extent, he is allowed to grasp the upper edge of the transom and pull himself up and inboard while the rescuer standing in the stern sheets assists by catching him under the arms and pulling. The center of gravity should be kept low and the efforts of both should coincide.

When the victim is unable to aid himself he is brought inboard in the same manner as that prescribed heretofore for lifting a victim from the water onto a low dock or float unassisted. This technique applies also to cases in which the rescuer must get into the boat himself before hauling the victim aboard.

Occasionally, the task of getting the victim into the boat is quite beyond the strength of the rescuer. In this case, the victim's arms are pulled inboard until the chest is against the transom. If the arms are then lowered to rest on the stern seat, the victim can be held with little difficulty until help arrives or until a method can be devised to secure him or bring him inboard.

A victim brought into the boat in a conscious state will

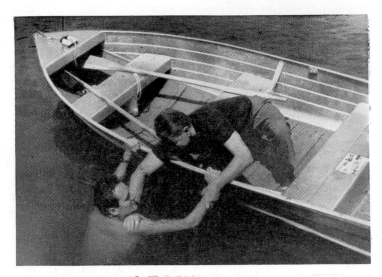

Fig. 117. Position for preventing victim from overturning boat.

Fig. 118. Rowboat rescue. Holding victim and reentering boat.

usually take a reclining position in the stern sheets. There he may rest and recover somewhat on the way to shore and if any evidence of hysteria or shock develops the rescuer should take such measures as are necessary to counteract it.

What to do with a victim in the boat when it is discovered that he has ceased to breathe is a problem not easy to solve. Conditions vary so much that only general principles can be given which may be applicable to any given situation. The immediate requirement of the victim is air, and artificial respiration is indicated. If the boat is so constructed that it is possible to place the victim in prone position and administer effective pressure, this should be done. If this is not feasible the victim should be left draped over the stern just as he has been hauled inboard and all speed should be made to shore. If the rescue has been effected a long way offshore and the return journey will be a matter of more than two or three minutes every effort should be made to apply artificial respiration rather than to row to shore. Thus, the victim may be laid over a thwart;

Fig. 119. Holding victim against transom.

he may be shifted to the deck of a motorboat if, as frequently happens, one appears on the scene. These are suggested as possibilities but solution of the problem attendant on such a situation must depend largely upon the wisdom and ingenuity of the rescuer himself.

Paired Boat Rescue.—Many of the foregoing difficulties cited would be completely eliminated if boat rescuers could go in pairs. The ideal arrangement is to have two persons in the rescue boat even if one may have but little knowledge of rescue methods. Thus, one can give his whole attention to handling the boat, while the other keeps the victim in sight and directs the oarsman. He can also assist in hauling the drowning person aboard. Where it is necessary for one rescuer to go over side after the victim, the other will remain with the boat and maintain its position. Finally, the problem of starting artificial respiration or going ashore becomes no problem at all, since one may row and the other resuscitate.

Motorboat Rescue.—As the use of the small motorboat increases it will be used for rescue purposes even more frequently than now. The methods used in rowboat rescue are applicable to the small motor craft with little adaptation. Two conditions, however, create an element of danger in effecting a rescue with a power craft; one, the relatively high speeds at which even the smallest of them may operate, and the other, the unguarded propeller revolving at high speed. It has been known to happen that the rescue boat has run down the victim and in several instances the victim and sometimes a rescuer in the water has come in contact with the rapidly rotating screw.

The implication is obvious. Rescue motor craft should close in on the victim at greatly reduced speed and should be so directed as to pass and make contact from the side. Just before actual contact, the clutch should be slipped and the screw stopped. If, as in the case of outboard craft, there is no clutch, the motor should be stopped and the boat allowed to drift in the few remaining feet.

Small Sailing Craft Rescue.—Operators of small sailboats are usually so skilled in handling their craft that they need little instruction for approaching a drowning victim. All that needs to be said is that the course should be so directed that the boat may be rounded to and come up to the victim in much the same manner as that employed in picking up a mooring.

Surf Rescue

The turbulent water conditions prevailing on open beaches require special knowledge, special forms of technique and in some cases, special equipment to make rescues effectively. Fundamental knowledge of wave-action, undertow, tide currents and, above all, surf bathing *experience* is necessary before anyone may attempt any but the simplest of wading rescues in surf. The pool and inland swimmer may be quite expert

Fig. 120. Using ring buoy for surf rescue.

in swimming, boat handling and life saving in the quiet waters to which he is accustomed, but when he comes to the open shore of the large lake or the sea his past experience will serve him poorly until he has familiarized himself with surf conditions and adjusted his aquatic abilities to new and different demands. Stroking, rowing and carrying will require a new rhythm in which the action of the waves will be an added element. First attempts will be sorry ones but in a surprisingly short time, if the swimmer takes it slowly and easily, the adjustment will be made; but to become truly expert in surf rescue one must adopt the formula of experience—experience and more experience.

All of the methods employed in making wading and throwing rescues in quiet waters can be used in surf. The hand reach, the ring buoy and the heaving line have all been used successfully over and over again but with due regard for different water conditions. Reaching rescues are timed to hold against receding movements of the water and to use the force of oncoming waves to assist in gaining the shore. Bringing a person landward by means of a ring buoy or a heaving line is not merely a matter of hauling him in hand-over-hand. The rhythm of the onrushing breakers and the intervals of slack water in between must be considered and their forces utilized if the victim is not to be hauled under water or the line or buoy torn from his grasp. In essence, a skill is required which is not unlike that displayed by an angler in playing a game fish.

The Human Chain.—The human chain is a device especially useful in rendering aid in shallow water where undertow or current makes it particularly dangerous for one to venture alone to the rescue. Four, five or six people lock wrists swiftly and form a chain. The anchor man stands secure in thigh-deep water while the chain extends far enough to enable the outermost person to seize the victim and bring him to safety. This device can well be used also in streams and lakes.

Fig. 121. The human chain employed in surf.

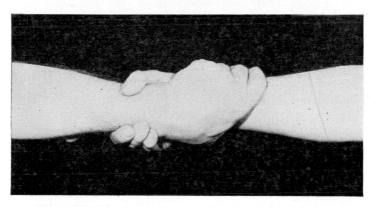

Fig. 122. Interlocking wrist grip for human chain.

Swimming Rescue in Surf.—On open beaches, drowning accidents usually occur not as a result of foolhardiness but because of lack of knowledge of water conditions and unforeseen or unperceived changes taking place. Thus, undertow, runout or change in the set of the tide may carry the bather out from shore with startling rapidity and often before he is aware of his predicament. Also, swimmers sometimes make their way out beyond the breakers and find that they cannot get back.

Swimming rescues under such circumstances are often quite unlike those made in calmer waters. If the surf is high and pounding, the approach to the victim may be difficult and exhausting. When the rescuer reaches the victim he may find that support and reassurance are needed more often than actual rescue measures. The return journey to the beach may sometimes be made only with great difficulty or may even be impossible without auxiliary aid.

The rescuer should whenever possible take some buoyant but not unwieldy device with him for a swimming rescue in surf. An inflated rubber swimming tube, a ring buoy or a surfboard will serve very well. Any one of these will aid in keeping the victim afloat until additional help arrives or until it can be determined how best to get back to the shore.

The Swimming Rescue Buoy.—The best piece of surf rescue appartus yet devised is known as the torpedo buoy. It is so designed and rigged that it can be taken out through almost any surf; it can be used as a support for not only one but several victims, if necessary. By means of a line attached to it, the connection with the beach need not be broken if the victim is within range.

This buoy is a watertight torpedo-shaped shell made of metal divided into three watertight compartments. It is compactly constructed being only three feet six inches long and not exceeding ten inches in its greatest diameter. A life line is looped along its length on both sides. From an eye in the nose, a short lead line extends which is bent into a loop at the end. To an eye at the opposite end of the buoy three hundred feet of light but stout trail line is secured by means of a snap hook. This line is usually wound on a reel to keep it from fouling. The torpedo buoy can be used without the line but, wherever possible, connection with the beach should be maintained.

Efficient use of the torpedo buoy requires a crew of two or, better, three persons, one to take the buoy out to the victim, one to stand midway along the line in waist-deep water and hold a part of the line clear of the surf and the third to tend the

Fig. 123. Crew from buoy rescue in surf.

reel and, after contact is made, to haul both rescuer and victim to shore.

To make a rescue, the buoy man seizes the torpedo and casts the loop of the lead line over one shoulder and under the opposite arm. Carrying the buoy by the looped life line he wades outward as fast as he can under the conditions. At a point, usually where he begins to meet the big "breaks," the buoy is dropped and the rescuer starts to swim, towing it behind him. Meantime, the reel man tends the reel and line and the line man wades outward holding the trail line high above his head and allowing it to slip through his hands.

When the victim is reached, if he is able to help himself somewhat, he is allowed to seize the buoy and slide his head and chest up a little way over the outer end, grasping the life line at the sides of the buoy to maintain his position. The rescuer directs and assists him in this maneuver and then slides to the rear and takes a similar position reaching under the victim's arms to get a handhold on the life line. The position taken is very similar to that taken in sliding on a sled in prone position. When handholds are secure and all is in readiness the rescuer signals the reel man and the buoy and its load are hauled in hand-over-hand by pulling on the trail line. The reel man plays a very important part in this type of rescue. He must play the line to take advantage of the wave action, to hold against adverse currents and to maintain those hanging to the buoy in reasonable comfort. He must handle the line himself with such assistance as he may need from the line man and one of his major tasks will be to prevent onlookers from laying hold of the line and running it up the beach. In their eagerness to assist, these well-meaning bystanders can tear the buoy from the grasp of both rescuer and victim leaving them at the mercy of the waves.

Fig. 124. Position on buoy for coming ashore.

An unconscious victim or one who is so exhausted as to be quite unable to help himself in any way requires a little different treatment. In this case the rescuer makes a rear or front approach in the usual manner, levels and assumes a cross-chest

Fig. 125. Position taken to come ashore with helpless victim.

carry. By means of his lead line, he draws the buoy to him and secures a grip on the life line near its nose, signals the reel man and is drawn ashore.

Sometimes it happens that it is better to use the torpedo without the trail line. The rescuer may be alone or the victim further from shore than the trail line can reach. In this case, the rescuer has two courses open to him; either to swim to the victim and use the buoy for support until additional help arrives on the scene or he may give one end of the buoy to the victim and swim to shore, either towing by means of a handhold on the opposite end or swimming free in the loop of the lead line.

The use of the torpedo buoy is not limited to the surf alone. It can have a place and may well be used for swimming rescue at any swimming beach of sizable area.

Other forms of surf rescue buoys such as the diamond or can buoy are employed in rescue in essentially the same manner as the torpedo buoy.

Swimming Rescue without Equipment.—Where no equipment is available and a swimming rescue must be made, the procedure in surf is quite similar to that employed ordi-

Fig. 126. Using rescue buoy without trail line.

narily; that is, the manner of approaching and carrying is the same in principle but requires some adaptation.

The swim out from the beach will be complicated by the inrushing breakers and requires ability to go over or through them without losing too much ground. Contact will be made either with the rear or front approach, rarely under water. The carry will be a matter of selection. Beyond the breakers any of the carries may be used but in most cases the head carry will prove most satisfactory, inasmuch as the oncoming waves can be watched by the rescuer in this position, and his leg strokes so timed that the victim's head and face may be held clear of each crest.

Taking a victim in through the breakers is a task which requires that the rescuer use all his resourcefulness, strength and knowledge of the kind of surf he is combating. As a general rule the rescuer shifts the victim into a cross chest carry just before he reaches the outermost breaker. Every inrushing breaker should be caught and ridden in as far as possible with the rescuer stroking vigorously and striving to keep pointed toward the beach. The interval between breakers when the rescuer lies in a weltering trough should be employed in keeping the victim's face above water rather than in making progress. The feet should go down and the rescuer stand only when the water is so shallow that the footing can be held against the back rush of the undertow. It is out of the question to keep the victim's head above water at all times in coming through the surf. Every breaking wave will bury both rescuer and victim as it passes and there is no help for it.

For a victim who is swimming helplessly but because of the odds against him is making little or no progress, a free swimming rescue method has been devised which not only permits the rescuer to aid the victim effectively but also keeps him in a much more favorable position to avoid being drowned in the surf.

From a position fronting the helpless swimmer the rescuer seizes the wrist exactly as he would in a surface approach but instead of turning him about, tows the victim in swimming position by one extended arm allowing him to aid by swimming with the free arm and the legs. The position is a good one since it permits the victim to take waves and breakers on the back of the head rather than directly in the face.

Should the victim become frightened and attempt to climb up the arm to the rescuer's head and shoulders, the towing arm should be quickly relaxed and a foot brought up against the victim's chest to hold him away until he recovers his wits. If he continues in his struggles to grasp the rescuer, the victim must be turned about and placed in a cross chest carrying position.

Boat Surf Rescue.—Boat rescue in quiet waters is quite

possible for anyone who knows the rudiments of rowing and boat-handling. On the surf beach, however, quite the opposite condition exists. There only the most highly skilled surf boat-men can make a boat rescue. The mere launching of the boat calls for a degree of skill which can be acquired only through long practice, and rowing in breakers calls for courage and re-sourcefulness as well as skill.

Surfboats vary greatly in size and structure all the way from the six-oared self-bailing boat of the Coast Guard used in shipwreck down to the simple one man dory-skiff found on pleasure beaches. In principle, however, they are much the same, light enough to be readily maneuverable, yet of sturdy construction to withstand the pounding they get from the waves. The best of the type are higher in the bows and stern than amidships and have higher sides than boats of the same size in inland waters. The surfboat is somewhat longer and a bit broader of beam than boats of corresponding type found in quiet waters. If the surfboat is large enough to require a steers-man, a long steering oar is used in preference to a rudder. A rudder may be unshipped and rendered useless by the plunging action of the boat in rough water or when the stern is tossed upward may be completely out of water at a time when it is needed most to hold the boat on its course. A long steering oar, on the other hand, is always in the water and its leverage is so great that the maneuverability of the craft is greatly increased. Pulling oars should be light and stiff for greater ease in han-dling.

Little need be said here of the larger types of boats for special usage, notably the Navy whaleboat and the Coast Guard surfboat. These require years of training by the crews for the exacting tasks they are called upon to perform. The great skill displayed in putting such boats through heavy surf com-mands great admiration but there should be no desire on the part of the average rescuer to develop like skill. Professional and volunteer life guards on surf bathing beaches should, however, seek to develop genuine skill in handling smaller boats for surf rescue.

Small surf rescue boats may be handled by one man or a crew of two or three. Where the surf is only moderate in height and intensity one oarsman or a rower and a steersman may take a boat out and return very well. Paired oars are used in such cases. When the surf is bad, however, a three man crew is most effective, one man to an oar on separate thwarts and a steersman in the stern. Certain principles govern the handling of the boat no matter what its size, the number of its crew or the condition of the surf.

Once the boat is fairly launched and water borne, the oarsmen take their places and ship the oars. If there is a steersman, he keeps the boat pointed by holding to the stern until the oarsmen are in place before he takes his place. The first principle in running out or in, for that matter, is to keep the boat pointed at all times. Pointing the boat means to hold it squarely at right angles to the oncoming seas. If it is allowed to veer even slightly the breakers will swing it broadside to the waves in short order and cause it to fill and capsize. On a flat beach the breakers will be small for some distance from the water edge and the boat can be gotten under way without serious trouble. On a steep beach, however, the large "breaks" will be closer to the shore and the space in which to get under way will necessarily be short. Under the latter conditions the oarsmen must "put their backs to it" if they are to gain momentum enough to ride and split the crests of oncoming waves and pass beyond them rather than have the boat thrown back and rolled over. The ideal manner in which to work a boat out through surf is to so maneuver it by alternately holding and giving way as to have the waves break either ahead of or behind the boat. This cannot always be done and when the boat does have to meet a wave just as it breaks, sheer momentum is the only thing which will enable it to get through.

If, despite the momentum or because of the lack of it, the boat is up-ended or veered sharply by an oncoming sea and it is evident that it will capsize, the crew should lose no time in leaping clear of the boat and away from its swing or fall to avoid being crushed as it overturns.

The slough or run-out which ofttimes has carried bathers seaward and put them in jeopardy, can sometimes be used as a runway for the rescue boat. The current running directly outward not only helps to speed the boat on its way but it also flattens out breakers in its path and makes the job of getting the boat beyond the surf much less difficult.

Once beyond the breakers, rowing and steering is much less difficult as there is little danger of filling or capsizing. If the boat is partially filled with water and it responds sluggishly to the oars a little time must be taken to bail. The rescue crew then proceeds to the victim. When the victim is picked up and brought inboard in the usual manner, the boat is turned and headed back to the beach.

As the lifeboat nears the surf again a new problem develops; namely, how to run inward through the breakers. Two courses of procedure are possible. If the waves are not very high, the crew may elect to run in bow on but success in this maneuver depends upon the skill with which the boat is pointed and held on its course. Following seas run under the boat lifting the stern high and burying the nose deep in the forefoot of the wave. Even a slight deviation from the course at this time causes the stern to start swinging sharply, the boat broaches to and capsizes as it rolls broadside to the wave. The other course which may be followed with greater safety is to turn the boat outside the surf and back in stern foremost, alternately pulling ahead to meet oncoming waves and backing sharply in the intervals of slack water. This maneuver also requires great skill.

On steep beaches where the break is close to the shore it is customary to wait outside the break until a good-sized wave rolls in, then to bend to the oars with all strength and ride the wave into shallow water where the oarsmen can leap over-side and run the boat up on the beach before the next wave crashes in. This is definitely a crew maneuver and should not be attempted by one man.

It can be seen that rescue by means of a surfboat is a com-plicated procedure which may take some time in heavy seas. For surf rescue of victims not more than two hundred yards from shore, it is customary on well-guarded beaches to send a swimming rescuer with a buoy through the surf to reach and support the victim while the boat is being manned, launched and rowed to the rescue. Often a good swimmer can get through a heavy surf more easily than a lifeboat.

Surf bathing beaches are generally supervised by profes-sional life guards of long experience. It is not unusual for a life guard to spend ten or fifteen successive seasons at the same beach and in that time he has ample opportunity to learn the surf and tide conditions peculiar to that beach. If he keeps in good physical trim by constant training and activity and stays abreast of life saving trends and new developments in tech-nique, the supervision he offers will be adequate. The preven-tion of water accidents and the safeguarding of bathers are his sole responsibilities. Consequently, the intrusion upon or the usurpation of his duties by visiting swimmers and life savers no matter how well trained, may be resented. Amateurs well trained in life saving who habitually frequent a beach can serve best as auxiliary volunteer members of the regular corps of life guards, to assist in supervising bathing on days when the crowds are large. The association of amateurs and profession-als on any beach depends largely upon the establishment of cordial relationships based upon a common interest in the wel-fare of the bathers. If this is true of surf bathing beaches it is no less applicable to any bathing place where amateur and pro-fessional life savers commingle. For life savers who visit bathing places only infrequently whether amateur or professional, their status is the same as that of all other bathers and they are subject to all general restrictions. They should neither expect nor seek exception because of their abilities.

Until that time comes when all surf bathing beaches are completely and adequately supervised by guards appointed for the purpose there will be a need for life saving knowledge and ability within the ranks of the bathers. No person trained in life saving should feel that he has had complete training and experience until he has learned to adapt his knowledge and technical equipment to the surf. Then only will he be able to tackle the problem of a surf rescue with full courage and some assurance.

Canoe Rescue

A canoe should not be considered ordinarily as a piece of rescue equipment because of the fact that in any but the most experienced hands, it has not the stability needed for use in hauling drowning persons from the water. There are times, however, when an emergency arises in which a canoe is the only craft available for rescue purposes or is nearest to the scene of the accident. It can be used then but only by those who are well practiced in handling canoe rescues. If the canoeist is a good swimmer, can paddle and maneuver a canoe handily and knows and has practiced the various forms of canoe rescue, he may be considered to have the ability to attempt a rescue.

No less than five different emergency situations can be visualized in which a canoe rescue may be attempted. Each requires a variation in technique and a different method of handling. The situations and procedures follow. All are described as one person operations. Where there are two paddlers in the canoe, the second one will serve to steady the craft while the first makes the rescue. The procedures detailed below describe a group of possibly typical situations. However, it must be borne in mind that no two rescues are exactly alike. Wind and water conditions, type of canoe used, personal ability of the rescuer and reaction of the victim, all tend to introduce individual problems which have to be solved as they arise. Definite practice with a volunteer subject under a variety of conditions is absolutely essential; likewise, it is important that the rescuer himself should act as a subject during practice. The problem of giving resuscitation, if it is indicated, may be complicated due to bodily injuries received as a result of careless or improper handling of the victim during the actual rescue. Only by having personal experience as a subject can the rescuer realize the importance of careful handling.

Rescue of a Tired Swimmer.—A tired swimmer, even though apparently not panic-stricken, should be approached with caution in order to avoid an impulsive attempt to grasp the gunwales heavily enough to upset the canoe. The psychological value of calmly reassuring the swimmer is important. He may then be approached head-on, in which case he will grasp the bow, where there is but slight danger of actually overturning the canoe. While he is momentarily resting, the rescuer moves to a seated position in the bottom of the canoe amidships; the swimmer is then told to move hand-over-hand along the gunwale until he is near enough to be assisted by the rescuer if necessary while climbing aboard. The weight of the rescuer concentrated low in the center of the canoe makes it possible to counterbalance the weight of the swimmer while climbing in.

Rescue of Capsized Victims.—When a rescuer in a canoe arrives at the scene of a capsizing, if no victims are visible it is advisable immediately to go alongside and by grasping first the keel and then the gunwale roll the capsized boat or canoe towards him to right it, since it is possible that someone may be underneath. If no one is discovered, it is possible to begin surface diving at once by first securing the canoe by means of its

Fig. 127. Canoe-over-canoe rescue, first step. Have victim hold onto the end of your canoe; roll the other canoe over.

Fig. 128. Canoe-over-canoe rescue, second step. Lift the end in over your canoe about three feet and then roll it bottom up and slide it to a balanced position across your canoe.

Fig. 129. Canoe-over-canoe rescue, third step. Roll the canoe upright again and slide it back into the water.

Fig. 130. Canoe-over-canoe rescue, final step. Hold the two
canoes together firmly while victim climbs in.

painter to some part of the swamped craft which will then act
as a sea-anchor to prevent undue drift. If a victim is clinging
to the bottom of the craft but indicates that another has disappeared, the condition of the visible one will govern the rescuer's decision as to whether to take him aboard first and then
proceed as previously outlined, or to have this victim attend to
holding the canoe while surface diving is undertaken. If the
victim or all victims are visible, their condition will determine
whether or not any consideration should be given to the rescue
of the craft; the safety and care of the victims being the first
and most important factor.

In general, the approach is from the leeward side in order
to avoid being pounded down upon the capsized craft and injuring the victim. If possible, the victim is drawn in or gets
aboard across the bottom of his craft. In case of two unconscious victims with wrists lashed together, the rescuer should

grasp the bound wrists or get the paddle blade under them and lift them toward the bow of the rescuer's canoe where they can be hung on either side. The wrists of one can then be secured with the painter and the bindings unlashed. First one and then the other can be lifted aboard.

If the victims are all right, recovery of the canoe or small rowboat may be undertaken. This should be rolled right side up, or the victims may be instructed how to do this before moving around their craft to hang on the bow and stern of the rescue canoe. The bow of the swamped craft is then lifted slowly, and brought across the gunwales of the rescue canoe amidship; it is then rolled upside down and pulled across until it balances, empty of water; the near gunwale is then grasped and the craft rolled upright, when it may be slid back into the water ready for further use by its original occupants.

Rescue of an Actively Drowning Person.—An actively drowning person cannot wait very long for assistance, cannot be reasoned with and will not listen to instruction as to how to get into the canoe. The rescuer should lose no time in driving his canoe alongside of the victim but just out of reach. The blade of the paddle is thrust into the grasp of the victim. The paddle will be used as much for holding the drowning person away from the canoe as to support his head above water.

It happens frequently that the victim will make every effort to seize and endeavor to climb into the canoe. If he does get a grip on the gunwale the rescuer may use either of two tactics. If the canoe is fairly broad in the beam and stable, he may hold the victim's hands or wrists with one hand and by placing the other hand on the shoulder prevent the victim from heaving his upper body above the gunwale. If he cannot get his weight over the gunwale, he cannot force it under water. If the canoe is not very stable, his convulsive movements may cause it to dip sharply and be in danger of filling. In this circumstance, the rescuer may slide overboard on the opposite side and by hold-

Fig. 131. Extending paddle to actively drowning victim.

ing to the gunwale and using his weight seek to counteract the victim's pressure on the other side thereby preventing the canoe from rolling over. If the drowning person is more scared than actually drowning he will occasionally have enough strength to breast over the side and climb into the canoe. The rescuer may then slide to an end of the craft and get in. But if the victim cannot climb inboard he will tire rapidly and finally hang on to the canoe using no more effort than is necessary to keep his face above water. Watching his opportunity the rescuer may quickly reenter the canoe, seize the victim's wrists and shoulder and prepare to haul him inboard in the same manner as that employed for the unconscious person or the tired swimmer. Another method of control to prevent the panicky efforts of the victim from capsizing the canoe, is to move quickly to a seated position in the bottom of the canoe amidships from which position balance may be maintained and the frenzied actions of the victim counteracted.

Rescue of a Floating, Unconscious Victim.—In the rare case in which a victim is still afloat even though unconscious when reached, the rescuer should have no hesitancy in running in alongside the victim and reaching over side to seize him by the hair or arm. The paddle is then placed in the canoe and the rescuer settles his weight as low as possible just back of amid-

Fig. 132. Lifting unconscious victim into canoe.

Fig. 133. Finishing the lift of an unconscious victim into canoe.

ships. Two courses are now open to him by which he may bring the victim inboard. He may turn the victim's face toward the canoe and by pulling on the wrists lift the victim's upper body and bring it in over the gunwale. Then, by adjusting the position, the victim is hitched inward until only the legs remain in the water. The upper body may then be swung forward and the rescuer can grasp the legs and bring them inboard. The other method of procedure requires that the rescuer float the victim face up alongside the canoe and parallel to it. The near arm and leg are lifted inboard as far as possible and hooked over the gunwale. The rescuer then reaches across the victim's body and grasps one side of the bathing suit or clothing and rolls the victim into the canoe. Both of these methods require some strength and considerable dexterity to get the victim inboard and at the same time balance the canoe. Rescuers whose strength is not adequate to the task have the alternative of grasping both wrists of the victim in one hand while steadying themselves on the gunwale with the other and carrying the victim towards the stern of the canoe until the arms can be passed over the end with the curve of the stem snugly fitted into the shoulder. The wrists may now be lashed in this position with painter, belt or necktie so that he may be towed towards shore. When under way, the relaxed body will trail, thus throwing the head forward to be cradled between the shoulder and the side of the canoe with the face clear of the water.

Rescue of a Submerged Victim.—Attempting a rescue from a canoe of a victim who has disappeared beneath the surface is a task beset by many problems. It is apparent that the rescuer must leave the canoe and dive for the drowning person. If the rescuer is alone it becomes a real problem to retain control of the craft even though away from it. Some means have to be devised to hold it in the immediate vicinity so that it may be recovered when the rescuer returns to the surface. An empty canoe is a very buoyant thing which will drift very rapidly before even the lightest breeze. Two methods have been devised for controlling the canoe, which seem to have survived the test of time and experience.

In certain sections of the country the use of canoes is widespread. A person who possesses and uses one habitually for exercise and enjoyment will find it a great convenience to have the canoe equipped with a bow and a stern line or painter. One of these may be of the conventional three or four foot length to be a utility line for tying-up, et cetera. The other may be practically the length of the canoe, to serve as an emergency line. The simplest manner of fastening both lines is to bore a small hole through the triangular deck-piece, pass the line through it and knot it underneath. The free end of the utility line may be whipped or back-spliced, but the end of the emergency line should be provided with a small eye-splice. In order that the long line may not be continually getting adrift or fouled, it should be just long enough, when dry, to lead beneath the thwarts and hook onto the head of a screw placed beneath the deck at the opposite end of the canoe, then by springing it to one side it may be hooked back of the projecting ends of the bolts that hold the thwarts. In this manner it leads practically along the entire length of the gunwale, out of the way, yet available at an instant's notice.

When an over-board rescue is attempted, the eye-splice on the emergency line is doubled back to form a slip noose which may be placed on one ankle of the rescuer, or may be thrown over the head, across one shoulder and under the opposite arm. The rescuer may then go over-board, dive deeply and even swim about under water, and still retain control of the canoe. Care must be exercised to avoid fouling the line or becoming entangled. If the rescuer considers it to be a long extension of his own person which will follow wherever he may go, he will govern his action accordingly.

Getting back into the canoe and hauling the victim aboard is the same procedure as that which is used to bring a drowning person on to a low dock or platform unassisted. The rescuer clamps the victim's hands on the gunwale near one end of the canoe, breasts out and, turning, brings the victim inboard in the same manner as that described heretofore for canoe rescue of an unconscious victim.

Another method of holding the canoe near the scene of the accident while searching for a submerged victim is that of deliberately capsizing the craft before starting the search. A capsized canoe will float readily and support both rescuer and victim when they return to it. Because of its partial submersion the speed of its drift will be greatly reduced and the rescuer will be able to regain it without difficulty upon his return to the surface. The rescuer, upon reaching the canoe, must haul the victim far enough across it to rest the head and arms upon the upturned bottom, clear of the water. He may then direct his efforts to steadying the canoe until help arrives or to swimming it and its burden to shore.

Canoe rescue is difficult since it requires the rescuer to operate from an unsteady base. It demands not only foreknowledge and practiced skill but resourcefulness and a fine sense of balance as well. These requirements put it quite outside the province of the unskilled canoeist and life saver.

Surfboard Rescue

The surfboard as a piece of rescue apparatus has been for hundreds of years a unique development belonging almost wholly to the islanders of the south Pacific, notably in the Hawaiian Islands. Since the advent of the new type of hollow surfboard and with the use of balsa wood, on the mainland of the United States and because of its unrestricted usefulness in all waters whether coastal or inland, it has become a rescue device of universal appeal and interest and as such is taking its place as an extraordinarily effective piece of rescue equipment. Because of its handiness and the speed with which it can be driven through the water it surpasses in rescue effectiveness any other type of equipment, including the boat. Swimming rescue is slow in comparison.

To use the surfboard for rescue requires that the rescuer should be a good swimmer and thoroughly skilled in paddling and maneuvering the board. His ability to make rescues with it will depend upon the extent of his skill and his knowledge of and practice in the various methods of rescue to which it is adapted.

The surfboard in rescue work is much like a canoe. It has even less stability than the canoe but in compensation it is not affected by being overturned. The surfboard can be taken through broken water where a canoe could not even be launched. Because it lies very low in the water with its upper deck almost flush with the surface, much of the difficulty of lifting and sliding a person aboard is eliminated. It has buoyancy enough to support four persons on its deck or a dozen hanging to its sides.

The surfboard can well be the most important piece of rescue apparatus on any bathing beach and as such it deserves a place. A life guard or a swimming instructor thus equipped is a far more effective person for his job.

Taking Off from the Beach.—The surfboard is kept on the beach during swimming hours. It may rest upright against the guard tower or horizontally on a rack at one side.

To start to the aid of a bather in difficulty, the rescuer seizes the board midway along the side and holds it under one arm, the fingers gripping the lower edge. The other arm is stretched forward along the upper edge to control the board and prevent it from swinging. With the board held in this position, the rescuer runs into the water and when he reaches ankle depth crouches and drops the board a little forward and flat on the surface. Without checking his momentum, the rescuer flings himself on the board with the lower hand still gripping the edge, the other laid forward on the deck and with one foot on the board. Actually, he is supporting himself at three points with the body held somewhat above the board. The board meanwhile is sliding swiftly outward over the water much like a bobsled gliding over snow. The rescuer adjusts his balance quickly, sinks to a prone position and without breaking momentum, starts to paddle.

Approaching.—In quiet waters, the paddle out to the victim is simply a matter of pointing the board and using either the crawl arm stroke or the double over-arm for propulsion.

For approaching through surf, the technique is not quite so simple. The three principles which applied to taking a boat out through surf apply also to the surfboard; namely, the bow of the board must be pointed squarely at the oncoming breakers at all times; there must be sufficient momentum to carry

Fig. 134. Approach stroking on surfboard.

over and beyond the "breaks"; good judgment is necessary in selecting the spot at which to go through and for timing the "break."

Small breakers crested with a foot or so of foam can best be ridden through by seizing the edges of the board and lifting the body clear of the deck allowing the crest to wash along the board beneath the body. This position is identical with the front leaning rest in gymnastics.

Meeting large waves as they break presents a condition which requires much skill on the part of the rescuer. When it is apparent that a big one must be taken, the rescuer may do one of two things. He may gain his utmost momentum then flatten out on the board head down, hands extended forward and gripping the edges and try to go through it, or he may slip off the board at the side and tilt it on edge to lessen resistance.

As the rescuer nears the victim he sights along the board and lays his course a few inches to one side of the drowning person.

Contact.—Contact is made without slackening speed. As the board rides by, the rescuer reaches out and seizes the victim's wrist or arm and holds it firmly. The light weight of the board and the drag of the victim's body combine to check headway and bring the board to rest.

The rescuer comes to a sitting position astride the board with the feet and legs in the water to aid in stabilizing the board. The victim's arms are then pulled across the board until his chest is against the edge. The rescuer places one hand on the victim's arms and the other on his shoulder, thereby holding him in good position for breathing but effectively preventing any attempts to climb onto the board.

When wits and breath are regained, the rescuer seizes the back of the victim's bathing suit and slides him on the board a few inches at a time, gradually swinging the head forward until

Fig. 135. Contacting victim on surfboard.

Fig. 136. Victim under control.

he is lying at full length. The rescuer then lies forward with chest on the victim's legs and paddles ashore. If the victim has lapsed into unconsciousness, his head may be pillowed on the forearms with the face turned to one side.

Fig. 137. Sliding victim onto board.

Coming Ashore.—Regaining the shore in quiet waters is simply a matter of paddling straight ahead. Coming ashore in surf presents much the same problems as those which are met in bringing in a boat under the same conditions. The point at which the board comes in should be chosen carefully; the rescuer should contrive wherever possible to let the "break" come either ahead of or behind his board. If caught by a comber, he

Fig. 138. Returning to shore.

can keep the board pointed and prevent it from nosing into the bottom by sitting up and shifting his weight well back toward the stern, contriving meanwhile to hold the victim's legs and grip the edges of the board with his hands. When the comber passes he should resume paddling.

Other Types of Surfboard Rescue.—A submerged victim can be rescued from a surfboard by using a light line attached to the stern of the board and carried in a loop over the shoulder of the rescuer in much the same manner as it is in making a similar type of rescue with a canoe. The line should be not more than twenty feet long. The expert surfboard handler will stand upright on his board as it rides over the spot where the victim was last seen and will do a front header from it. After recovering the victim, the rescuer will bring him back to the board, hold the arms, and push up to swing to a sitting position prior to taking the victim onto the board.

An expert surfboard handler can haul a capsized canoe across his board, right it and slide it back into the water more easily than it can be done over another canoe. The operation is performed from the sitting position but the low deck of the surfboard quite offsets this handicap.

CHAPTER IX

ICE ACCIDENT PREVENTION AND RESCUE

A considerable section of the United States lies far enough north to be subjected in winter to periods in which freezing temperatures prevail. In the extreme northern belt, lakes and streams are covered with sheets of ice early in the season which get thicker and stronger as the winter deepens and do not melt until the coming of spring. Progressing southward the season of solid ice on the ponds and streams becomes shorter and shorter. Six weeks of firm ice, four weeks, then good ice only during an occasional cold snap and finally, in the deep south, no ice at all. To the people of the extreme northern states the coming of the ice is a normal annual event and upon its arrival a season of healthful out-of-door sport begins. Skates are brought out not to be put away again until early spring. A few degrees of latitude to the south, the ice sport season is shorter but just as enjoyable. Further south a sudden cold snap may serve to bring thousands to the lakes and streams for a brief day or two of skating before the mercury climbs once more and the ice softens. Regardless of the degree of latitude, however, the problems connected with preventing accidental drowning by breaking through the ice are much the same everywhere. However, the knowledge and experience of those who live in the extreme northern states where the skating season is an annual event, enable them to recognize hazardous conditions rather more quickly than others. But even there ice accidents occur and the loss of life by drowning through the ice is much too great. The problem of venturing onto the ice safely depends largely upon knowledge of two kinds, namely, **where** one may skate safely and under **what** conditions.

Where to Skate.—Small bodies of water such as pools, ponds, flooded hollows, slowly flowing streams and small lakes generally offer the safest and the best conditions for out-of-door skating. These freeze more quickly than larger bodies of water and the ice formed upon their surfaces is more apt to be smooth and remain longer. Ice formed over swiftly moving water, or water the level of which is constantly changing, is likely to be unsafe for skating no matter how thick. Ice on small swift streams, large fast-flowing rivers and over tide water is subject to constant wear or strain. The only condition under which it is at all safe to venture upon ice of uneven or unknown quality is that in which the depth of the water beneath the ice is not above the waist and even this may be hazardous if there is a swift current flowing beneath it.

Safe Conditions for Ice Skating.—It is impossible to discuss the question of how thick the ice should be for skating except in the most general terms because of its great variation in quality. In general, ice may be considered on the basis of age. Newly formed ice is frequently referred to as young ice. Ice which is firm and solid, as it is during a prolonged freeze, is known simply as good or firm ice. Ice that is being subjected to the assaults of hot sun and warm winds in the early spring is commonly called old or rotten ice.

Young ice is formed during the first freeze of the winter season, or is formed in flooded hollows or over old ice after a midwinter thaw. In its first stages it is quite transparent and because the darkness of the water beneath shows through, it is sometimes known as black ice. Young ice may be extremely tough and elastic; that is, it may crack in all directions under the weight of a person, yet not give way but it is not really safe for skating until it has frozen to a depth of at least two inches and even then skaters should venture cautiously and not congregate in groups upon its surface. When young ice reaches a depth of four inches, it will support large numbers of skaters without buckling.

In the new ice season there are two major conditions which menace skaters; first, they may venture onto its surface before the ice is thick enough to bear the weight and second, the ice may not be of uniform thickness over the entire area. In the latter case, the ice may be but a thin crust over springs welling up from the bottom and at the inlets and outlets of feeder and draining streams. Furthermore the ice is quite likely to be weaker toward the center of pond, lake or stream. Obviously, the safe procedure in the early skating season for anyone is to wait until the ice is really firm enough to bear the weight and then to stay reasonably close to the shore, avoiding those areas previously mentioned in which the ice is likely to be weak. It is likewise inadvisable from the safety point of view to skate alone, especially at night. It should be remembered also that new ice weakens under the midday sun or with any rise in temperature. Ice that was as tough as steel at dawn may be weak as wet tissue at noon.

With continued freezing temperatures the ice thickens and strengthens until it is the firm ice of midwinter. As the thickness of the ice increases and snow falls, melts and is converted into added layers, the quality of the ice changes. No longer is it transparent but rather bluish white. A foot of this kind of ice will support the weight of skaters, horses, even automobiles. At this season there is little danger to skaters though quite often the surface is spoiled for skating by the presence of snow. Only at night is there real danger when possibly the skater may glide into an area of open water left by the ice-cutters or into the "blow-hole" caused by ice pressure.

The season of the old or rotten ice comes as winter ends and spring advances. Warm winds and hot sun batter away at the structure of the ice, loosening its crystals and honeycombing its surface until it shatters and dissolves in the waters beneath. At this time no one should venture on the frozen surfaces of rivers, lakes or ponds even though the ice may appear to be solid. Two feet of what looks like firm ice may be so saturated with water that the lightest pressure may cause it to crumble and vanish in a few seconds leaving open water in its place.

Methods of Self-Rescue after Going through the Ice.— There are, at least, two general rules of conduct which are applicable to all cases in which a person breaks through the ice. One, he should not attempt to climb out immediately and two, the feet should be kicked to the surface to the rear to avoid jackknifing the body beneath the ice rim to which the person is clinging. If the ice is quite thin or greatly weakened by cracking, the first instinct of the skater, which is to get out of the water as quickly as possible, will cause him to press up over the edge of the weakened ice and result only in another broken area and another plunge beneath the surface. Instead of reacting in this manner the skater should extend the hands and arms forward on the unbroken surface before him, kick to an extended and nearly level swimming position, and work his way forward onto the ice. If it breaks again, he should simply maintain the same position and slide forward once more. Eventually ice firm enough to bear the weight of the extended body may be reached and once upon it the skater may squirm or roll away from the broken area.

Contrary to popular conception, skaters in motion do not plunge straight downward into the water when the ice gives way beneath them. Instead they are tripped by the edge of the unbroken ice before them and are sent sprawling. It is then that they do usually, precisely the wrong thing. They try to get to the feet and skate away from danger. In getting to the feet they concentrate all the weight over one small area and then really break through. Whereas if they hug the surface of the

Fig. 139. Squirming to safety with the aid of ice awls.

ice in the prone position to which they have been thrown and begin to squirm or roll toward firmer ice, the chances are that nothing more serious will happen than getting the feet wet.

Ice Accident Rescue and Rescue Equipment.— Through recklessness, carelessness or merely lack of knowledge of ice conditions, literally hundreds of persons break through the ice each winter and of these some are drowned. Many northern cities provide for ice sports in their parks by maintaining cleared areas of ice on ponds or streams or artificially created skating rinks. These areas are supervised and when the ice is considered safe enough for skating, a white flag with a red ball at its center is flown at a conspicuous point. Since, however, almost any town or city has nearby many bodies of water which are frequented by skaters and since supervision cannot be afforded to all those who skate, it is customary to provide rescue equipment of one sort or another and to place it on the shores of ponds or streams where it can be reached and put to use quickly in an emergency.

Probably the best device for such use is the light ladder and line. This is merely a lightly constructed ladder some fourteen to eighteen feet long. To the lowest rung is attached a light but strong line coiled ready for use. To effect a rescue this ladder is lifted from its rack, laid flat upon the ice and shoved end on to the person in the hole. If the ice is weak for a greater distance than the length of the ladder from the hole, the line may be used as an extension and the ladder shoved outward to the extreme limit of its length and the length of the line attached to it, as well. The rungs of the ladder offer excellent handgrips by which the victim may, if he is able, haul himself from the water and then lying at full length upon it with his weight consequently well distributed, he may be drawn quickly to safety. In case the victim's hands are so numbed by cold that he cannot seize and haul himself onto the ladder, a rescuer may crawl out along the ladder and aid the victim. Then even if the ice breaks beneath the double weight of rescuer and victim, the ladder will always angle upward from the broken ice area and can be drawn swiftly to safety by other skaters.

For ice rescues in which the rescuer must remain at some distance from the victim because of the weakened condition of the ice, a ring buoy with line attached or a coil of line with a weighted end is most useful. A ring buoy can be scaled along the ice to a victim in the water with remarkable accuracy and for a considerable distance. Likewise, a line weighted at one

Fig. 140. Using the ladder to make a rescue.

Fig. 141. The ice cross as a rescue device.

end with a hockey stick or a billet of wood can be skidded out across the ice to the person in jeopardy. If the ring buoy or stick cannot be held to by the victim because of numbness of the fingers, the line attached to it can always be placed by the victim around the body below the armpits which will enable the rescuers to haul him to safety.

A long light pole with a short length of line attached which ends in a large loop, is perhaps the best device for making ice rescues when the rescuer can with safety get reasonably close to the hole into which the victim has plunged. The loop may be dropped over the head and shoulders of the victim if he is unable to hold with his hands while being drawn out.

One other type of ice rescue device may be mentioned as being useful under certain conditions. This is the boat sled, a fairly high sided, flat bottomed punt with ends deeply undercut, and shod with four to six steel runners laid lengthwise along the bottom. This type of boat is found to be useful on sea ice and occasionally during the spring break-up of the ice on rivers, bays and large lakes. Persons are sometimes caught by the breaking up of the ice and carried away by tide or current on rapidly disintegrating ice floes. Amid the welter of open water, ice cakes and larger ice fields and floes, this type of rescue craft can be paddled or rowed when in the water. When ice obstructs the course, the boat can be run up onto it and slid along like a sled until open water is reached again.

This kind of boat requires a crew of three or four men equipped with oars or paddles, pike poles, and ice creepers for the shoes. Although not frequently seen, the boat sled is an excellent rescue device of which more use should be made where the conditions previously mentioned are likely to be found.

All of the aforementioned devices should be considered as ice rescue equipment, some form of which should be placed where it is likely to be needed and where its use can be controlled. It is argued that equipment of this kind cannot be left unwatched because vandals will misuse, destroy or appropriate it to their own use. It is quite true that this may happen but when the placement of such devices is coupled with a little education in the reasons why they are provided, plus a threat of legal punishment for theft or willful destruction, the ladder, pole or ring buoy will not be disturbed except in case of actual need. This has been the experience in a number of places where devices of this character have been provided for so long that there is no thought of disturbing them.

Extemporized Rescue Devices.—It is extremely doubtful if it will ever be possible to get all skaters to carry devices either for self-rescue or for the rescue of others whenever they go skating. Yet there are two things which can be carried by anyone if he so desires and which will help very materially in case of ice accident. A stout clasp knife in the pocket, especially one that has a short marlin spike fitted along the back, will, when it is driven into the ice at arm's length from the hole, aid one in drawing himself out of the water and along the ice to safety. A forty to fifty foot length of light stout line which can be put into use immediately is the best possible thing to have about one to aid another who has broken through. There are many ways in which a line can be carried on one's person without being a nuisance. It can be carried in a roll in the pocket, coiled inside of the hat or cap or it can be used to wrap the grip of a hockey stick in place of tape. If one end is secured to the stick and the other end so tied that it can be loosed and unwrapped quickly, one has not only the line, but the stick itself to carry the line out to the victim. For all around utility in making ice rescues, no simpler or more useful article can be found.

A typical thin ice accident occurs something like this: An unsuspecting skater or group of skaters ventures onto young ice of unknown quality and strength. At first they hug the shoreline timidly ready to flee at the first sign of ice weakness. Nothing happens and in the exhilaration of the sport they begin to sweep farther and farther away from shore, cutting figures, chasing one another in a spirited game of tag or indulging in just plain skating. The less marked the glassy surface the more attractive it is as they range to all parts of the pond or stream. Then one of two things may happen. A lone skater glides over a spot where the ice is too thin to bear his weight and breaks through; or a group of skaters, without thought of consequences, gathers in one spot to rest and talk. Suddenly the ice begins to crack and buckle beneath their feet; they scatter in all directions but all too often one or more of the group is too slow in getting away and plunges beneath the surface. Rarely does it happen that the victim does not reappear. Usually he is back at the surface trying frantically to climb out, almost at once. His struggles serve only to break more and more ice and exhaust him by his repeated duckings. Eventually, if he has a grain of sense left, he comes to rest.

Meanwhile, all the rest of the skaters on the pond converge as rapidly as possible upon the scene of the accident, coming as close as they dare to the struggling victim and producing again by their concentration of weight precisely the same conditions that may have caused the original accident. In many such situations the ice breaks again and another victim is left struggling in still another hole. Or, one more daring than the rest will skate in toward the struggling victim and try to reach him with an extended hockey stick. His weight alone or the combined weight of well-intentioned rescuer and victim, as he seizes the end of the extended stick and heaves himself upward, usually results in more surface giving way and in a trice, two are in jeopardy. Situations such as these described occur so frequently because of lack of judgment and no knowledge of how to proceed.

In an ice accident situation of this character, common sense should indicate, but often does not, what can and should be done. First, skaters should be warned away from the scene of the accident. Second, the victim should be told to "take it easy." He may not listen during his first mad scramble but when he tires, which will be soon, he can be told to extend his arms out along the unbroken surface and kick his feet to the surface to keep from jackknifing under the edge of the ice. Meanwhile, if any type of rescue apparatus is available, it should be obtained as rapidly as possible and used as heretofore indicated. If no apparatus is at hand, either one of two methods may be used for rescue, the human chain, or the plank or board.

To form a human chain, three, four or five strong individuals approach as closely as they can with safety, then one after another in single file, they drop down on the ice and begin to worm their way outward toward the victim. The first man has both arms free, of course, but each succeeding person in the file seizes the skate of the man ahead of him, thus forming the chain. When the first man gets within arm's reach, he seizes the outstretched arms of the victim by the wrists. Then slowly and cautiously the whole line begins to wriggle back to safety drawing the victim after it. If the ice breaks under the weight of the leading man in the chain, he can be held and drawn back to safety by the others.

The plank or board rescue is essentially a one man operation. Two planks or wide boards of as great length as it is possible to get are used to make the rescue. At the edge of the

Fig. 142. A rescue by means of the human chain.

weakened area the planks are placed on the ice headed outward. The rescuer lies at full length on one plank and shoves
the other ahead of him. He then worms his way onto the
second plank, draws the first one alongside and then shoves it
forward. Thus shoving first one plank and then the other ahead
of him and alternately transferring his weight from one to another, he may make slow but steady progress across many
yards of cracking and buckling ice to reach the victim where
he clings to his precarious hold. In the same way, the return
journey is made to firm ice or shore with the victim creeping
from plank to plank as they are advanced in essentially the
same manner as the rescuer.

One problem in ice accidents has always been and will
continue to be, what to do when the victim who goes through
the ice fails to get a handhold on the surrounding ice and disappears. It has happened many times in the past that a strong

and courageous swimmer has plunged boldly into the opening in an ofttime futile attempt to locate the victim and bring him to the surface. Although heroic in intent, too often it has resulted in the rescuer losing his own life or at least, endangering his life. Beneath the ice is a perpetual twilight zone and it is not only difficult but often impossible to locate the opening through which the rescuer descended, when he has to return to the surface for air. The mental agony attendant upon coming up beneath the ice can be readily imagined. It is difficult to say whether or not it is justifiable to attempt the rescue of a person submerged beneath the ice. It must be left in the last analysis to the judgment of the potential rescuer. If he is possessed of great courage, stamina and swimming ability, he may make the attempt but only upon one condition, and that is, if a stout line and someone to handle it is available. The line may be tied about the rescuer's waist, the free end placed in another's hands, and only then should he risk the plunge. If he does not appear again at the surface within a reasonable time, the line tender will haul upon the line to bring him up and by further hauling aid him in getting out of the hole and onto the ice.

Care of an Ice Accident Victim.—If a victim is not breathing when brought to safety, artificial respiration must be started just as soon as possible. The question occasionally arises, "Should artificial respiration be commenced at once in the open or should a little time be taken to carry the victim to the warm interior of a house or shelter?" This is a difficult question to answer since it depends so much upon the circumstances surrounding the accident. Of course, the immediate requirement of the apparently drowned person is oxygen, yet if the process of resuscitation is prolonged, the attempt to restore life to the victim will be defeated by the chilling of the body due to the wet clothing and the cold. If shelter is close by, it will be better, no doubt, to risk the few seconds it will take to get the victim to a warm interior before beginning artificial respiration. If there is no shelter within easy reach, restorative measures must be taken at the point where the victim is brought ashore and every possible effort must be made to keep him warm. Even while resuscitation is being applied, overcoats, sweaters, and blankets can be placed over and under the victim. Beneath the blankets, helpers may strip the wet clothing from the body if it can be done without interfering materially with the rhythmic action of resuscitation. Fires may be lighted close by for added warmth and as resuscitation proceeds, bricks or even stones may be heated, wrapped and placed along the sides and between the thighs.

Just as in any other drowning accident, when the victim is brought to safety still breathing but exhausted by his struggle, collapse and the development of shock must be guarded against. He should not be allowed to exert himself in any way but must rest in a reclining position while restorative measures are taken. While he is resting and regaining strength, the wet clothing should be removed, he should be wrapped in overcoats, sweaters or blankets and beneath the covering, rubbed dry and warm. The friction of rubbing is one of the best methods of restoring circulation to the chilled flesh. If any hot drink is available, it is administered if or when he can swallow. As soon as he is somewhat recovered, he should be transported to shelter where he can be put to bed to rest and recover. If the immersion has been at all prolonged or if there is any evidence of distress, a doctor should be summoned. The danger of pneumonia developing as a result of the accident is ever present.

In conclusion, it is well to sum up briefly the problem of ice safety. First, the safety of anyone on the ice depends upon knowing and being able to recognize safe as opposed to unsafe ice conditions. The first stages of ice formation and the last ones of disintegration are the two really dangerous periods of the skating season. Eagerness to get onto the newly frozen surface and reluctance to quit it as the skating season ends are the direct causes of most ice accidents. If the individual would wait a few days or even only overnight in some instances at the beginning of the season and would forego skating at the first signs of thawing, there would be far fewer ice accidents.

Second, there are certain types of ice rescue equipment and definite ways of making rescues which have been tried and have proved their worth unnumbered times. Making such equipment available and knowing how to use it or knowing how to make a rescue without equipment is of great importance to every skater. Ice rescues are almost always dangerous procedures for the rescuer, but equipment and knowledge of its use or ability to improvise rescue devices greatly lessen the hazard of aiding the unfortunate victim of an ice accident.

It is not intended to have anyone consider ice skating a dangerous sport. The purpose of this discussion is merely to indicate that there are hazards connected with it and that accidents do occur occasionally. The material presented is given here merely to indicate what to do to avoid the hazardous conditions and how to aid those who have the misfortune to get into difficulty.

INDEX